PARENTS' MAGAZINE'S
FAMILY QUIZ BOOK

Compiled by Gerard Mosler and the
editors of Parents' Magazine Press

Illustrated by Olivia H. H. Cole

Parents' Magazine Press · New York

Table of Contents

JANUARY

1	2	3	4
New Year's Day			L. Braille, 1809–52, invented reading system for the blind
5	6 New Mexico, the 47th state, admitted, 1912 F. D. Roosevelt's "Four Freedoms" speech, 1941	7 First national election in U.S. 1789 First boat through Panama Canal, 1914	8 Jackson Day, honors Battle of New Orleans, 1815, and Andrew Jackson, a founder of the Democratic Party
9 Connecticut ratified Constitution, 1788	10 Ethan Allen, 1737–1789, Revolutionary hero, leader of the "Green Mountain Boys" of Vermont	11 Alexander Hamilton, 1755 or 1757–1804, first Secretary of the Treasury, established Bank of the U.S.	12 Charles Perrault 1628–1703, French writer of fairy tales, *Cinderella, Sleeping Beauty,* etc.
13 George Fox, died 1691, English religious leader, founder of the Society of Friends	14 Albert Schweitzer, 1875–1965, humanitarian	15 Molière, 1622–73, outstanding French dramatist	16
17 Benjamin Franklin, 1706–90, Am. statesman and philosopher	18 Daniel Webster, 1782–1852, lawyer, statesman, defender of the Constitution	19 J. Watt, 1736–1819, Scottish inventor Robert E. Lee, 1807–1870, Leader of the Confederate Army	20 Inauguration Day
21 T. J. (Stonewall) Jackson, 1824–63, Confederate General	22 Francis Bacon, 1561–1626, English essayist George Gordon, Lord Byron, 1788–1824, English lyric poet	23 John Hancock, 1737–93, patriot, signer of Declaration of Independence	24 Gold discovered in California, 1848 First Boy Scout troop organized in England in 1908
25 Robert Burns, 1759–96, Scottish poet	26 Michigan, 26th state, admitted, 1837	27 Lewis Carroll (Charles Dodgson), 1832–98, English writer, creator of *Alice in Wonderland*	28
29 Thomas Paine, 1737–1809, wrote, "Rights of Man" Wm. McKinley, 1843–1901, 25th U.S. President	30 Franklin D. Roosevelt, 1882–1945, 32nd President	31	

TRUE YEAR—OR FALSE?

Can you tell how many of the statements about our calendar listed below are TRUE?

With a score of 9 and over you are TIMEwise.

1. New Year's Day has not always been observed during the last 200 years. T F
2. George Washington was born on February 11, 1732. T F
3. Abraham Lincoln was born on February 12, 1809. T F
4. The month of July was named after Caesar. T F
5. Christ was actually born in the year 4 B.C. T F
6. The year 1900 was not a leap year. T F
7. The year 2000 will be a leap year. T F
8. Easter may never fall before March 22 or April 25. T F
9. January was the eleventh month in the Roman calendar. T F
10. The calendar in use today is called the Gregorian calendar. T F
11. The Ides of March is March 15. T F
12. After common law a half year consists of 182 days. T F

TRUE WINTER—OR FALSE?

Can you tell how many of the statements about the winter season, listed below, are TRUE?

With a score of 9 and over you are TRUEly WINTERwise.

1. It is sometimes too cold to snow. T F
2. No inhabited place is as cold as the North Pole. T F
3. The heating of city buildings raises the outdoor temperature. T F
4. Black frost does not exist. T F
5. Blizzards cannot accurately be forecast by the Weather Bureau. T F
6. The coldest winter on record was that of 1888. T F
7. Sound travels faster in clear winter weather than in summer. T F
8. North Dakota has below-zero weather for a longer period than any other state, excluding Alaska. T F
9. The world average precipitation of snow and rain is 160,000 tons. T F
10. Hail rarely falls during winter. T F
11. The coldest winter weather usually comes when the days are shortest. T F
12. Sea water freezes at 27° Fahrenheit. T F

COMPETITIVE WORD GAMES FOR ALL

THE SHORT WORD WINS!

Find the *shortest possible* word by adding as FEW letters as possible to *each* side of each letter pair. (No S-endings or proper nouns!) Example: 1. tHRow. Score 1 point for each letter added, 10 points when you are unable to make up a word. In some instances you will be able to find a word *shorter* than the answer provided. Par score is 34 points.

1. _____H R_____   7. _____E N_____
2. _____A A_____   8. _____W Y_____
3. _____P E_____   9. _____Y P_____
4. _____P Y_____   10. _____E P_____
5. _____Y W_____   11. _____A A_____
6. _____N E_____   12. _____R H_____

THE LONG WORD WINS!

Find the *longest possible* word that can be spelled from the letters in each of the words below. Score as many points for each word as it has letters. Example: 2. Get the word RAGE from the word AGREE and score 4 points for it. In some instances you will be able to make a *longer* word than the answer provided. Par score is 78 points.

1. _____HEART   7. _____ENVIRONS
2. _____AGREE   8. _____WISTERIA
3. _____PRAISE   9. _____YESTERDAY
4. _____POSTER   10. _____ESPIONAGE
5. _____YARDAGE   11. _____ALTERATION
6. _____NUCLEUS   12. _____RHINOCEROS

A DUCKY PROBLEM

There are two ducks here that are alike and carry the same flower; there are two other ducks that are alike and carry a different flower; and finally, there are two ducks that are not alike but carry the same flower. Can you find these ducky pairs?

WHO'S WHO IN THE AMERICAN CITY DIRECTORY?

Match each American city with the famous person it is named after. A score of 18 and over is good.

1. Audubon, N. J.		a)	American antislavery novelist
2. Bessemer, Ala.		b)	English navigator, explorer
3. Boone, Ia.		c)	American patriot
4. Brigham, Ut.		d)	American poet
5. Burbank, Cal.		e)	President
6. Carnegie, Pa.		f)	Puritan leader, governor
7. Cudahy, Wisc.		g)	French missionary, explorer of Canada
8. Decatur, Ill.		h)	Polish-American revolutionary general
9. De Soto, Mo.		i)	American novelist (*The Marble Faun*)
10. Euclid, O.		j)	German philosopher, author, explorer
11. Franklin, N. H.		k)	American ornithologist
12. Fulton, Mo.		l)	French general, aide of Washington
13. Greeley, Colo.		m)	Founder of American Mormon Church
14. Hancock, Mich.		n)	Inventor of a steel making process
15. Hawthorne, N. J.		o)	First signer of Declaration of Independence
16. Humboldt, Tenn.		p)	American editor and reformer
17. Lafayette, Ind.		q)	Scottish-American manufacturer and humanitarian
18. Marquette, Mich.		r)	Steamboat inventor
19. Pulaski, Va.		s)	American pioneer and frontiersman
20. Raleigh, N. C.		t)	American horticulturist
21. Revere, Mich.		u)	American meatpacker
22. Stowe, Pa.		v)	American writer, statesman, inventor
23. Tyler, Tex.		w)	Greek mathematician
24. Whittier, Cal.		x)	American commodore
25. Winthrop, Mass.		y)	Discoverer of Mississippi

EYE Q. TEST

Here you can test your vision and your patience at the same time. Two girls are exactly alike. Can you find them?

10

'STATE'LY WORDS

By using the official abbreviations of two of our United States, you can form the words to answer the brief definitions. Example: 1 **S C ORE** is formed from **S**outh **C**arolina and **ORE**gon. A score of 18 of more and you have done a 'state'ly job.

1. Account	_ _ . . .	14. Kind of red	_ _ _ . .
2. Large country	_ _ _ _ . .	15. Begone!	_ _ _ . .
3. Settlement	_ _ _ _ _ . .	16. Pattern	_ _ _ . . .
4. Hoarfrost	_ _ _ . .	17. Blaze	_ _ _ _ . .
5. Indian capital	_ _ _ _ _ . . .	18. Rubber juice tree	_ _ _ . . . .
6. Disabled	_ _ _ . .	19. Brought down	_ _ _ . .
7. Informal note	_ _ _ . .	20. Argentine city	_ _ .
8. Lily	_ _ _ _ . .	21. Egg cells	_ . .
9. Poplar	_ _ _ _ . .	22. Milan opera	_ _ _ . . .
10. Settled	_ _ _ . .	23. Animal sound	_ _ .
11. Pastime	_ _ _ . .	24. Festival	_ _ _ . .
12. Chipped	_ _ _ _ . .	25. Baltic port	_ _ _ . .
13. Fluid rock	_ _ _ . .	26. Reconnoiter	_ _ . _ _

THE ACTIVITIES OF SEÑOR SOMBRERO

Señor Sombrero is a Mexican wearing his traditional hat, the sombrero. He is seen here engaged in four different activities, but from a bird's eye view, that is, directly from above. The problem for you is to detect what Señor Sombrero is doing in each of the pictures. To make the task easier for you, we have anagrammed the captions for the pictures, and if you correctly unscramble all letters, the correct caption will result.

1. _ _ _ _ _ - _ _ _ _ _ _ _ (RETAILS METAL)
2. _ _ _ _ _ - _ _ _ _ _ _ _ (SLICED BAY RICE)
3. _ _ _ _ _ _ _ _ _ _ _ _ (LOLLS ON SABLES)
4. _ _ _ _ _ _ _ _ _ _ _ _ (KISS EAR WING)

GET THE BANDIT BEHIND BARS ! ! !

A re-discovered age-old Chinese board game provides
intriguing new entertainment for all family members

This game is based on an old Chinese legend about a bandit whose depredations in a village resulted in the decision of the inhabitants to drive him into the local temple and there capture him. The bandit was extremely clever, and the inhabitants found they had a difficult time to chase him into the temple. How the chase proceeds and how the bandit tries to protect himself is explained in the rules below. A posse of 16 inhabitants are given the task of driving the bandit into the temple. This game requires two players, one representing the posse and the other, the bandit.

THE RULES OF THE GAME:

1. There are 17 figures in the game: 16 members of the posse and 1 bandit. (Take 16 pennies and 1 quarter as in sketch.)

2. Place the members of the posse at the intersections around the board. Place the bandit in the center.

3. The game is played by two players. The bandit's aim is to escape. The posse aims to drive the bandit toward the temple and eventually to capture him there.

4. The bandit moves first.

5. Both posse and bandit may move in any direction—horizontally, vertically, or diagonally, but only from one intersection to the next.

6. The bandit may capture members of the posse when he finds any two are placed next to him on a horizontal or diagonal row—provided these two men are not separated from each other by an intersection. The bandit may then take two captives, but he loses his turn when he does so and must stay put for one move. When two posse members are next to each other on a vertical line, they cannot be captured.

7. When three members of the posse are next to each other on a row or diagonal the bandit may capture only the two closest to him.

8. The bandit defends himself by staying as far away from the temple as possible. If the posse succeeds in driving the bandit into the temple, and occupying its three corners, the bandit has lost the game.

NOTE: The posse members are not permitted to checkmate the bandit on the board so that he is unable to move. If this occurs, the posse has lost the game.

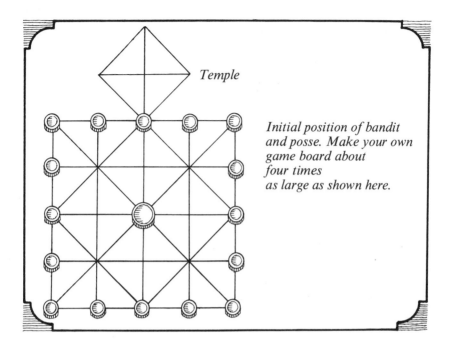

Temple

Initial position of bandit
and posse. Make your own
game board about
four times
as large as shown here.

WHICH WORDS HAVE ALL THE VOWELS?

Here is a vocabulary test if ever there was one! All words omitted in the following story (but to be guessed from the context) are words that contain all the five vowels (A-E-I-O-U) just once. How many of these all-vowel words can you find? A score of 15 and over is excellent.

As a rule, a man who occupies a 1) S B R D N T position of relative 2) N M P R T N C is not called in by the president of the company in a 3) C N S L T T V capacity. John Doe, however, was an exceptional young man enjoying a splendid 4) R P T T N for being upright in his 5) B H V R, 6) V R C S in his speech, precise and never 7) Q V C L, humorous but not 8) F C T S, quiet and 9) B S T M S in his way of life, sociable enough but not 10) G R G R S. Although his parents had been in rather 11) P R C R S circumstances John had received an 12) D C T N and soon 13) T D S T N C D his classmates in achievement. For all these reasons he was justly a 14) F V R T with all his fellow workers who, after considerable 15) P R S S N on their part, had finally been able to show him their trust when they 16) T H R Z D him to speak for all of them.

They knew he would exercise all possible 17) P R C T N so that the interview with the boss (who was believed to be in a rather 18) N F R G V B L mood) could be conducted without any 19) P R T R B T N for either party and thus the 20) X C L P T N of the unjustly accused co-worker attained.

ASSOCIATIVE CANCELLATIONS

Each of the persons listed below in alphabetical order can be associated with just one of the pictures. Example: Lincoln and stovepipe hat (1D). When all the names are matched with the pictures, six unmatched pictures will remain. The initial two or three letters of these remaining pictures, when read from left to right and top to bottom, will result in an old proverb.

Bell, Cinderella, Cleopatra, Columbine, Cupid, Damocles, Daniel, Diogenes, Edison, Eve, Helen of Troy, Tom the Piper's Son, Jacob, Jill, Lincoln, Little Bo-Peep, Noah, Pandora, Rembrandt, Romeo, Siegfried, Snow White, Wright.

TEASERS AND POSERS FOR YOUNG AND OLD

1. METHOD IN NUMBERS

No more than two minutes for this problem, or you will never get it anyway! Can you tell in just what order this string of numbers has been arranged?

8, 5, 4, 9, 1, 7, 6, 3, 2, 0

2. IN 'PLANE' VIEW

Which area within the square is the larger one: The one occupied by the vertical, or the one occupied by the horizontal strips?

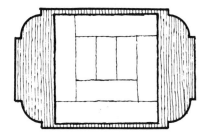

3. ARE YOU A CUBIST?

How many cubes are contained in this diagram?

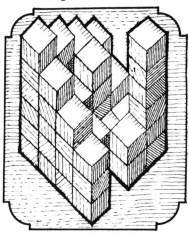

4. SQUARE MAGIC

There are 16 squares here, formed by matches. By re-arranging only four matches, you can make 17 squares.

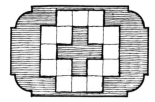

5. CANADIAN SPEECH

The inhabitants of a Canadian town speak either French or English, or both: 73% speak French and 87% speak English. What percentage speak both languages?

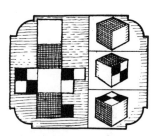

6. ANOTHER CUBE PROBLEM

If you mentally fold the plane figure shown on top, which cube would you get as a result?

7. PENNY WISDOM

From a pile of 13 pennies remove seven, then add five and have a pile of twelve. How do you do it?

ARE YOU A GAME DETECTIVE?

The children at play here are all missing their toys. Nevertheless, you can deduce what toy is missing in each instance by closely studying the positions and movements of each child. Moreover, we have listed some phrases below that can be anagrammed into the correct words for the missing toys. Example: 1) 1 MARBLES. Match ten or more pictures with the correctly anagrammed toys and you have played your part very well!

a) Pot
b) Board won war
c) Tatler
d) Tapering tow
e) Is led

f) To score
g) F.O.B. to all
h) Ho ho Paul
i) Tab all babes
j) Wings

k) Was See
l) Blamers
m) Panel
n) Pike pops ring
o) Slits T

THE NUMBER GAME

Each symbol stands for the digit of a number. The same symbols denote the same digits, of course. Your task is to execute the arithmetical operations so that the equations in all rows and columns will become true.

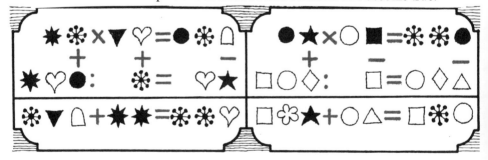

WHAT GOES ON IN THE LETTER CIRCLE?

Here is a new kind of vocabulary and information test. It is a kind of cross-word puzzle, but the answers do not go up and down and across. Rather they go around and around. Clues appear in the list below—one set for youngsters, the other for adults. The answers to both sets are telescoped into the circle of letters, and appear in clockwise order. Note that the ending of one word may be the beginning of the next word; and both names and words are hidden in other words, and so on. With nothing to write in, and the answers right in front of your eyes, it all looks very easy but, as you go on, you will not find it quite so simple. Example: The answer to A) The universe is ALL (29–30–31). A score of 16 or more in each category is good.

FOR YOUNGSTERS	FOR PARENTS
A) The Universe	A) "Steam engineer"
B) Patriot Ethan _____	B) Cuddle
C) Finish	C) Girls' patron saint
D) Experiment	D) Johnson or Jackson
E) Presidential first name	E) Only Jackson
F) Recent	F) Certify
G) Steam engine inventor	G) Party
H) Loan	H) Carroll
I) Label	I) Card
J) Mineral	J) Boat
K) Alice's grinning adviser	K) Abraham's home
L) Hastened	L) Goes with England or Mexico
M) Number	M) Stage family
N) Exists	N) Sound
O) Bird's home	O) Strip
P) Girl's name	P) English spy in Revolutionary War
Q) Large weight	Q) Great _____ (of China)
R) Conjunction	R) Long or short
S) Naval hero	S) "Green Mountain Boy"
T) Painted	T) "Right or wrong" man

17

FAMILY QUIZ GAME

From the *Parents' Magazine* popular FAMILY QUIZ GAME, we have culled the most interesting questions and packaged them under one specific heading for each member of the family. Keep in mind that this family fun feature is not designed to test intelligence but to provide interesting material for question-and-answer games the whole family can enjoy.

FOR MOTHERS:

FAMILY RELATIONS

(1) What is the Greek name of the wife of Zeus? (2) What legendary hero shot an apple off his son's head? (3) In *Uncle Tom's Cabin* the wife of Uncle Tom is _____ . (4) Who was King Arthur's wife? (5) What is the real name of Lyndon Baines Johnson's wife? (6) Three of Henry the Eighth's wives had the same name. What name? (7) Queen Elizabeth I was a member of what famous English family? (8) Name the four sisters in Louisa May Alcott's *Little Women*. (9) In the Bible, how long did Jacob labor before he could finally marry Rachel? (10) What was the name of Abraham Lincoln's wife?

FOR FATHERS:

PHILOSOPHY

(1) What Greek philosophical school, founded by Zeno, held that the passions and appetites should be rigidly subdued? (2) The doctrine that pleasure and happiness is the chief good and end of man is called _____ . (3) With what German philosopher do you associate the following: "Life has value only when it has something valuable as its object." (4) The science of correct reasoning is called _____ . (5) What well-known English philosopher wrote a work entitled *Mysticism and Logic*? (6) What philosopher described democracy as a "charming form of government full of variety and disorder"? (7) With what kind of explosion do you associate Thomas Malthus? (8) *Cogito, ergo sum* means _____ . (9) Was Karl Marx German or Russian? (10) What writings did Socrates leave under his own name?

YOUNGSTERS (5–6 YEARS):

ANIMALS

(1) Do animals get toothaches? (2) Name the animal from which we get bacon. (3) True or false: a female lion has no mane. (4) What bird is said to make the sound "gobble, gobble"? (5) What color is a polar bear? (6) A baby deer is called a _____ . (7) What bird is the tallest of them all? (8) What animal's roar is the loudest? (9) Is an alligator another name for a crocodile? (10) One would be most likely to find a black bear (a) on the desert, (b) on a beach, (c) in the mountains.

FOR JUNIORS (6½–9 YEARS):

THE BIBLE

(1) How many days and nights did it rain during the Great Flood? (2) What famous character in the Old Testament was afflicted with boils? (3) Name the shepherd boy who killed Goliath. (4) Tell with what he slew him. (5) According to the Bible, _____ was the first man on earth. (6) Where did he and his wife live? (7) True or false: Christ was born in Jerusalem. (8) Who was found in the rushes along the Nile River? (9) Who interpreted Pharoah's dream? (10) How many sons did Jacob have?

FOR TWEEN-TEENS (10–12 YEARS):

SPORTS & GAMES

(1) In baseball, the pitcher and catcher are known jointly as the _____ . (2) The Davis Cup is awarded for (a) swimming, (b) golf, (c) tennis. (3) In baseball, who is the "man in blue"? (4) True or false: Hockey can be played on ice and on land. (5) How many playing cards are there in a standard deck? (6) Not counting ties, what is the largest number of games that can be played in a world series? (7) The 1960 summer Olympic Games were held in _____ . (8) For what sport is Stan Musial famous? (9) By what name, other than castle, is a certain chessman called? (10) Babe Ruth's real name was _____ .

FOR YOUNG TEENS (13–15 YEARS):

PHYSICS

(1) Does sound travel faster through air or water? (2) When aluminum is heated it _____ . (3) The scientific name for Northern Lights is _____ . (4) Which gas is lighter: helium or hydrogen? (5) What gas is most abundant in our atmosphere? (6) What is the velocity of sound? (7) The chemical formula for carbon dioxide is _____ . (8) The erg is a unit of _____ . (9) Most of the world's diamonds come from _____ . (10) True or false: Pitchblende is the ore that yields uranium and radium.

LADYBUG

Only two ladybugs are exactly alike. WHICH?

ARE YOU ON THE BALL?

If so, you will be able to deduce, by employing sheer logic, the color of the scooter.

A DOZEN DOGS IN ONE!

Concealed in the letter maze there are at least 12 well-known breeds of dogs. Move horizontally, vertically, or diagonally, and repeat letters as often as necessary to spell out the name of a breed. Example: Start with the lower S, go to C, from there to O, double the T, move to I, then E—and you have Scottie. A score of 9 or more is good.

 # FEBRUARY

CALENDAR OF MEMORABLE DATES

1 Feast of St. Bridget, a patron saint of Ireland

First meeting of U.S. Supreme Court, 1790

2 Ground Hog Day

3 Felix Mendelssohn, 1809–47, composer

Horace Greeley, 1811–72, noted journalist, said, "Go West, young man!"

4 Charles A. Lindbergh, 1902– , famous flyer

5 Dwight Moody, 1837–99, founded Moody Bible Institute

6 Massachusetts ratified Constitution, 1788

20th Amendment ending "Lameduck Congress," passed, 1933

7 Charles Dickens, 1812–70, English novelist and social critic

George Herman (Babe) Ruth, 1894–1948

8 Boy Scouts of America incorporated, 1910

9 Nebraska, 37th state, admitted, 1867

U.S. Weather Service established, 1870

10

11 Thomas Alva Edison, 1847–1931, foremost American inventor: electric light, phonograph, motion pictures, etc.

12 Lincoln's Birthday, 1809–65

13

14 St. Valentine's Day

15

16

17 National Congress of Parents & Teachers (PTA) organized in Washington, D.C., 1897

18 Bunyan's *Pilgrim's Progress* published in England, 1678

19 Ohio, 17th state, admitted, 1803

20 Fredrick Douglass, died, 1895, slave-born abolitionist

U.S. purchased Virgin Islands from Denmark, 1917

21

22 George Washington's birthday, 1732–99

23 Johann Gutenberg, died, 1468, inventor of printing from movable type

George F. Handel, 1685–1759, wrote "Messiah"

24

25 Enrico Caruso, 1873–1921, famous tenor

26 William Cody, "Buffalo Bill," 1846–1917

27 Henry W. Longfellow, 1807–62, renowned American poet

Marian Anderson, 1903– , Negro singer

28

21

LOVE IS SO COMPLICATED

As a special treat for St. Valentine's Day, we have listed below, in alphabetical order, a number of the world's leading lovers of fact and fiction. Now it is an inescapable truth that the amorous adventures of these most famous lovers have been far from smooth. To refresh your memory of the enormous complications which these lovers had to cope with, we have printed in the form of newspaper headlines the most important affairs but have omitted the names of lover and beloved in each instance. It is your task to select the names from the respective name pools and associate them correctly with each clue by putting the numbers into the spaces provided. Example: The answer for A) is 15 (Romeo) and 31 (Juliet). Complete 14 or more headlines correctly and you will be well prepared for some of the pitfalls that have made love so complicated for many a proverbial couple.

WHICH LOVER_____   _____WHICH BELOVED

A) _____ dares age old family enmity by wooing _____
B) _____ swims nightly through Hellespont to be near _____
C) _____ ventures into Hades to regain _____
D) _____ becomes monk after being forced to give up _____
E) _____ is visible only to the eyes of _____
F) _____ is saved from Indians by _____
G) _____ first only 'proxy' becomes husband of _____
H) _____ is stabbed by uncle for alienating _____
I) _____ kills himself falsely thinking lions had torn _____
J) _____ falls in love with statue vivified through prayers into _____
K) _____ jealously thinking her unfaithful smothers _____
L) _____ stabs himself in midst of battle believing himself betrayed by _____
M) _____ dares mother's wrath by wooing mortal _____
N) _____ tricked into sleep is delivered to his enemies by _____
O) _____ escapes from prison to meet fugitive princess _____
P) _____ finds in dying hour after life-long separation _____
Q) _____ disproves that "love is complicated" by happy marriage to _____

LOVERS

1. Abelard	10. Leander
2. John Alden	11. Orpheus
3. Antony	12. Othello
4. Aucassin	13. Pygmalion
5. Cupid	14. Pyramus
6. Dante	15. Romeo
7. Darby	16. Samson
8. Gabriel	17. John Smith
9. Harlequin	18. Tristan

BELOVED

19. Beatrice	28. Hero
20. Cleopatra	29. Isolde
21. Columbine	30. Joan
22. Delilah	31. Juliet
23. Desdemona	32. Nicolette
24. Eurydice	33. Pocahontas
25. Evangeline	34. Psyche
26. Galatea	35. Priscilla
27. Héloise	36. Thisbe

COMPETITIVE WORD GAMES FOR ALL

THE SHORT WORD WINS!

Find the *shortest possible* word by adding as FEW letters as possible to each sides of each letter pair. (No S-endings or proper nouns!) Example: 2. dRAw. Score 1 point for each letter added, 10 points if you are unable to make up a word. In some instances you will be able to find a word shorter than the answer provided. PAR SCORE is 35 points.

1. ____G	Y____	7. ____H	D____
2. ____R	A____	8. ____O	N____
3. ____O	D____	9. ____G	U____
4. ____U	G____	10. ____D	O____
5. ____N	O____	11. ____A	R____
6. ____D	H____	12. ____Y	G____

THE LONG WORD WINS!

Find the *longest possible* word that can be spelled from the letters in each of the words below. Score as many points for each word as it has letters. Example: 1. Obtain the word BEGOT from the word GOBLET and score 5 points for it. In some instances you will be able to make a word longer than the answer provided. PAR SCORE is 82 points.

1. ____GOBLET		7. ____HYPNOTIST	
2. ____RÉGIME		8. ____OBSTINATE	
3. ____OVERACT		9. ____GENEROSITY	
4. ____UTENSIL		10. ____DIETICIANS	
5. ____NIGHTCAP		11. ____ARISTOCRATS	
6. ____DOMICILE		12. ____YELLOWBACKS	

PLANES IN COLLISION

How many planes can you find within these entangled lines?

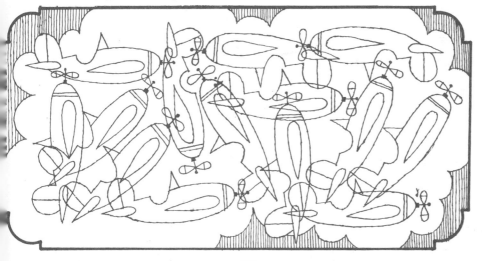

JOB-SEEKING ANIMALS

If it were possible to transform animals into human beings, which of the 26 professions in the right column would each of the animals in the left column be likely to undertake? In matching, try to do every animal justice. If you match 20 or more correctly, you qualify as head zoo keeper.

1. Dog	a) Pickpocket
2. Woodchuck	b) Miner
3. Bee	c) Brush maker
4. Elephant	d) Romeo
5. Musk deer	e) Upholsterer
6. Parrot	f) Wrecker
7. Mule	g) Radar operator
8. Cat	h) Dish washer
9. Pigeon	i) Weaver
10. Wolf	j) Spy
11. Spider	k) Actor
12. Raccoon	l) Pillow manufacturer
13. Horse	m) Juggler
14. Swine	n) Electrician
15. Termite	o) Announcer
16. Bat	p) Obstetrician
17. Badger	q) Watchman
18. Chimpanzee	r) Weatherman
19. Goose	s) Porter
20. Woodpecker	t) Perfumer
21. Fox	u) Messenger
22. Magpie	v) Singer
23. Stork	w) Trumpeter
24. Lark	x) Exterminator
25. Eel	y) Telephone lineman
26. Seal	z) Candymaker

SEAFOOD FROM THE LETTER FISH

Concealed in the letter maze are at least 15 well-known fish and shellfish. Move horizontally, vertically, or diagonally, and repeat letters as often as necessary to spell out the name of a fish. Example: Start with the B, go to A, then to S, which you may double, and get BASS. A score of 10 or more is very good.

ANIMALS WHO CAN TALK

Each of the people below can be described by the name of an animal. If you unmask 15 or more, you have done very well.

1. A sly person.
2. An idler or very lazy person.
3. A person of changeable character.
4. An extremely flirtatious man.
5. An imitator.
6. A person who repeats words without understanding.
7. A bold and greedy rogue or a rapacious swindler.
8. A dull and stupid person.
9. A doublecrosser.
10. A Northern sympathizer with Confederates.
11. An inhabitant of the State of Wisconsin.
12. A spiteful woman given to gossip.
13. A man at a gathering unaccompanied by a woman.
14. A person without spirit or courage.
15. A docile follower.
16. A notable person.
17. A speculator who seeks to depress prices.
18. A dealer who expects higher prices.
19. An inexperienced speculator.
20. A Detroit slugger.

CAN YOU GET THEM INTO THE CAGE?

By changing just one letter at each of the three steps under each animal, you can reach the cage with your fourth word step. Each letter change must result in a legitimate word. You have four animals to bring into the cage.

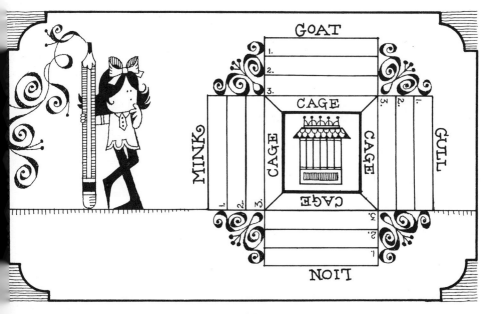

YOU BET YOU CAN

First dare your friends, then snare them with the tricks shown on these pages!

BET YOUR FRIENDS that you can break a slat of wood using only one hand.
HERE'S HOW: Place a thin slat of wood on the table so that about half of it protrudes from the edge. Lay a folded newspaper over the part lying on the table. Now hit the protruding part with your fist, and you will break the slat.

BET YOUR FRIENDS that you can push a half dollar piece through a hole the size of a penny.
HERE'S HOW: Cut a hole in the middle of a piece of paper. Fold the paper in half across the hole. Place the coin inside the fold, then bend the paper upward. The half dollar will drop easily through the hole.

BET YOUR FRIENDS that you can knock over a soda bottle without touching it or throwing anything at it.
HERE'S HOW: Place a soda bottle on a paper bag. Then blow the bag up, and you will see how fast the bottle will topple.

BET YOUR FRIENDS that you can crawl through a hole cut in a post card.

HERE'S HOW: Fold the card in the middle. Now cut it as indicated by the lines in our illustration, and the task is solved.

BET YOUR FRIENDS that you can, if tied to another person with strings as shown in the picture, free yourself without untying the loops.

HERE'S HOW: Take the middle of your partner's piece of string. Pass the string from the wrist up the palm of your hand through the loop, and then, pass it over all of your fingertips. You will then be free.

BET YOUR FRIENDS that you can tie a knot in a long piece of string without letting go of either end of the string.

HERE'S HOW: Cross your arms as shown in the picture. Then, still keeping your arms crossed, take one end of a piece of string in your right hand and the other end of the string in your left hand. Uncross your arms and the knot is tied.

MAKE A MATCH

This is a visual puzzle. For each *numbered animal* there is a corresponding *lettered object* with the same name. Example: 1. goose matches D. goose, an old tailoring iron. How many matches can you make? A score of 15 makes you perfectly matched.

RIDDLES, RIDDLES, RIDDLES

1. Where was the Declaration of Independence signed?
2. What is it that a person can place in his right hand that he can't place in his left hand?
3. Why do ducks and geese fly north in the springtime?
4. When is a wall like a fish?
5. What insect is found in school?
6. Why is a snake a careless animal?
7. What table is made of paper?
8. Why do movie stars keep cool?
9. What is it that is blind itself, and yet guides the blind?
10. If butter is 50 cents a pound in New York, what are window panes in St. Louis?
11. Who were the first people to do arithmetic?
12. There were 10 men in a boat. The boat tipped over and 9 got their hair wet. Why didn't the tenth man get his hair wet?
13. Where do little ears of corn come from?
14. Did Adam and Eve ever have a date?
15. What gallops down the road on its head?
16. Why did the city rat gnaw a hole in the carpet?
17. What is the difference between a donkey and a stamp?
18. Why is a banana like a sweater?

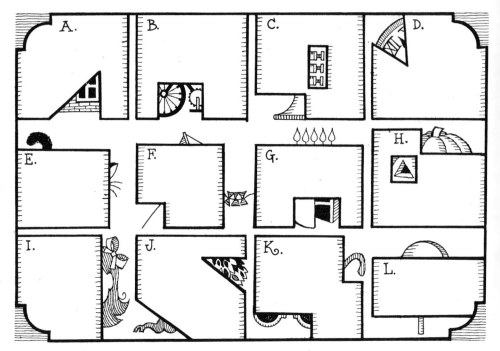

EYE Q. AND I.Q.!

How fast are you on the trigger? Here you can test yourself by guessing, in a race against time, what the partially concealed illustrations represent. Adults should be able to identify all 12 in three minutes. The youngsters are sharp if they can name 8 or more in five minutes.

TWO REBUSES FOR THE YOUNGER SET

Find the right words for the objects pictured in each rebus. Then add or deduct the printed letters as indicated. The result, in both instances, will be the name of a famous American. The answer to the first rebus consists of six letters. The answer to the second rebus consists of five letters.

WHAT GOES ON IN THE LETTER CIRCLE?

For directions on solving this puzzle, please turn to page 17.

For directions on solving this puzzle, please turn to page 17.

FOR YOUNGSTERS

A) Coloring matter
B) Early President
C) "Buffalo Bill"
D) Young sheep
E) Opposite of buy
F) Ulysses Simpson _____
G) Light bulb inventor
H) Busy insect
I) Grand Coulee
J) Hastened
K) Aria
L) Square root of 100
M) Cape _____, Mass.
N) Girl's name
O) Another girl's name
P) Old _____: Feb. 12
Q) Poster
R) Exist
S) Exists
T) Puerto _____
U) Tinted
V) Old form of you
W) State abbreviation
X) Alice's illustrator
Y) Thus
Z) Drop of sweat

FOR PARENTS

A) Ball
B) Caruso
C) Hard or soft
D) "Unconditional surrender" man
E) Stake
F) Part of the Trinity
G) Wonderland's artist
H) Buffalo Bill
I) Worker or soldier
J) Elia
K) Aswan
L) Happy Birthday, Old _____
M) Henry _____: Historian
N) Fish
O) _____ Louise Axson
P) Pittance
Q) Menlo Park wizard
R) Card
S) _____ Fitzgerald
T) Ruth
U) City in Oklahoma
V) Rail
W) Stain
X) Flee
Y) Measure
Z) Girl

31

FAMILY QUIZ GAME

For an introduction to this popular *Parents' Magazine* FAMILY QUIZ GAME, please turn to page 18.

FOR MOTHERS:

WOMEN

(1) What famous woman artist painted the popular painting "Horse Fair"? (2) Who was the famous duchess of whom Goya painted many portraits? (3) What is the title of Rachel Carson's book that awakened the nation to the dangers of pesticides? (4) Say *Mrs.* in French, Spanish, German. (5) An overly sentimental woman journalist is known as a _____. (6) Who was Othello's wife? (7) Name Mary McCarthy's best-seller about several Vassar graduates. (8) Xanthippe was the wife of what famous philosopher? (9) Name the heroine of the opera *La Boheme*. (10) Who was the "Swedish Nightingale"?

FOR FATHERS:

WAR

(1) The action in the book *For Whom the Bell Tolls* takes place during which war? (2) The two American generals who commanded UN forces during the Korean War were General Douglas MacArthur and _____. (3) Where was the battleship *Maine* sunk? (4) In what cemetery is the Tomb of the Unknown Soldier? (5) What was the final naval engagement of World War II? (6) In what year did Congress first exercise its power to declare war? (7) What two major events of the Civil War were terminated on July 4, 1863? (8) The Boxer Rebellion took place in a. India b. New Zealand c. China d. Japan. (9) True or false? Hungary was an Axis power during World War II. (10) The Hundred Years War was between what two countries?

FOR YOUNGSTERS (5–6 YEARS):
COMIC STRIPS & TV

(1) Can you name the family that owns a dog called Daisy? (2) The name of the dolphin in the TV show of the same name is _____. (3) On what program does Mr. Greenjeans appear? (4) True or false? Mr. Magoo is famous for his good eyesight. (5) Who is Archie's best friend? (6) Lil' Abner lives in _____. (7) Who created Donald Duck and Mickey Mouse? (8) Who are Deputy Dawg's constant companions? (9) _____ is the name of the man who can become Superman. (10) What is the name of the Lone Ranger's Indian friend?

FOR JUNIORS (6½–9 YEARS):
THE SKY

(1) Name the two planets closest to the earth. (2) True or false? A year is the time required for the earth to complete two revolutions around the sun. (3) Which is closest to Earth, the sun or the moon? (4) Constellations are groupings of _____. (5) Are we nearer the sun in summer or winter? (6) The largest planet in our solar system is a. Pluto b. Jupiter c. Saturn. (7) Does air have weight? (8) True or false? The sun is a star. (9) The two planets which have orbits smaller than the earth's are _____. (10) True or false? The sun revolves around the earth.

FOR PRE-TEENS (10–12 YEARS):
MUSIC

(1) The folk singer Josh White usually accompanies himself on what instrument? (2) To which musical family does the cornet belong? (3) How many strings has a ukelele? (4) There are _____ notes in an octave. (5) The Steinway family is famous for the manufacture of what kind of instrument? (6) A mouth organ is also called a _____. (7) The "Dance of the Sugar Plum Fairies" is from what Tchaikovsky ballet? (8) The composer Wolfgang Amadeus Mozart was born during the _____ century. (9) Chopin composed primarily for the _____. (10) How many sharps are in the key of D major?

FOR YOUNG TEENS (13–15 YEARS):
ABBREVIATIONS

(1) What does UNICEF stand for? (2) The letters I.Q.? (3) The initials NLRB? (4) The academic degree Ph.D.? (5) The letters A.M. on an average radio? (6) ICBM? (7) NATO? (8) SEATO? (9) NRA? (10) AEC?

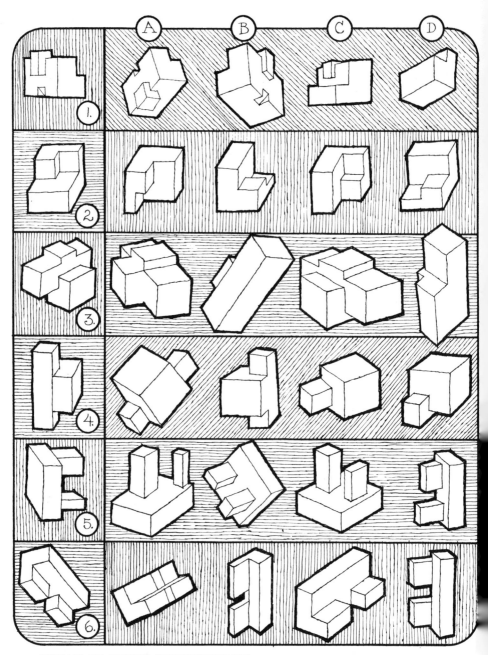

WHAT IS YOUR 'VIEW'POINT?

The problem is to determine which figure (A, B, C or D) is the figure on the left turned in a different position. Some figures must be turned over, others turned around, and some must be turned both over and around. Five or more correct and you have a good view on things.

MARCH

CALENDAR OF MEMORABLE DATES

1 Nebraska, 37th state, admitted, 1867	**2** Sam Houston, 1793–1863, Texas patriot	**3** Alexander Graham Bell, 1847–1922, inventor of the telephone	**4** U.S. Constitution declared in effect, 1789. Vermont, first state to be admitted, 1791
5 The Boston Massacre, 1770, five patriots killed by British	**6** Michelangelo, 1475–1564, foremost Renaissance artist. Elizabeth Browning, 1806–61, English poet	**7** Luther Burbank, 1849–1926, American botanist and plant breeder	**8** Oliver Wendell Holmes, 1841–1935, son of O. W. Holmes, poet, Justice of the Supreme Court, 1902–32
9 Battle of the Monitor and the Merrimack, 1862	**10** Salvation Army established in U.S., 1880	**11** Johnny Appleseed (John Chapman) died 1847. Blizzard of 1888 in New York City and New England	**12** Girl Scouts founded at Savannah, Ga., 1912
13 Standard time established in U.S., 1884. Joseph Priestley, 1733–1804, discoverer of oxygen	**14** Albert Einstein, 1879–1955, great physicist	**15** Maine, 23rd state, admitted 1820	**16** James Madison, 1751–1836, fourth President. U.S. Military Academy established at West Point, 1802
17 St. Patrick's Day honors famed Irish saint	**18** Grover Cleveland, 1837–1908, 22nd and 24th President	**19**	**20** First day of spring
21 First Indian treaty with Pilgrims, 1621	**22**	**23** Patrick Henry speech in Richmond, Virginia, "Give me liberty or give me death!" 1775	**24**
25 Arturo Toscanini, 1867–1957	**26** Palm Sunday. Robert Frost, 1875–1963, noted American poet	**27** Washington signed act creating U.S. Navy, 1794. Wilhelm Roentgen, 1845–1923, discovered X-rays	**28**
29 John Tyler, 1790–1862, 10th U.S. President. Niagara Falls froze over, 1848	**30** Alaska purchased from Russia, 1867	**31** Good Friday. Franz Joseph Haydn, 1732–1809, Austrian composer, "Father of the symphony"	

HOW ABOUT YOUR SUPERSTITIONS?

Whether or not you will "Beware the Ides of March" and therefore admit to some superstition yourself, you are probably familiar with this and many other superstitions. Now then, in the left column we have listed certain occurrences which the superstitious believe will result in the consequences to be found in the right column. If you can match 16 or more superstitious causes and consequences correctly, you know your superstitions well.

IF . . .
1. you drop a fork
2. a cat licks itself all over
3. you spill salt
4. a dog howls under your window
5. you find a four-leaf clover
6. you knock on wood or cross your fingers
7. you walk under a ladder
8. break a mirror
9. sit on a corner of a table
10. a black cat crosses your path
11. you toss salt over your shoulder
12. a white pigeon hovers over your house .
13. you feel itchy in your palm
14. you are the third on a match
15. you hear a cock crow in the afternoon
16. you see a shooting star
17. you hear a ringing in your ear
18. you see a spider at home
19. you hear a cricket inside your house
20. you put an article of clothing on wrong side out

YOU MAY EXPECT . . .
a) fulfillment of an innermost wish
b) luck on the third day
c) visitors will arrive soon
d) unexpected money
e) somebody far away thinks of you
f) a malicious mother-in-law
g) good luck in the household
h) death within a year
i) early marriage and engagement
j) to force good luck your way
k) things to go wrong for the rest of the day
l) domestic quarrel
m) fair weather
n) success
o) death in the family
p) bad luck for seven years
q) mishap on the same day
r) company is coming
s) fulfillment of a wishful statement
t) bad luck in the near future

COMPETITIVE WORD GAMES FOR ALL

THE SHORT WORD WINS!

Find the *shortest possible* word by adding as FEW letters as possible to each sides of each letter pair. (No S-endings or proper nouns!) Example: 3. vERy. Score 1 point for each letter added, 10 points if you are unable to make up a word. In some instances you will be able to find a word shorter than the answer provided. PAR SCORE is 39 points.

1. ____T H____
2. ____H C____
3. ____E R____
4. ____I A____
5. ____D M____
6. ____E F____
7. ____S O____
8. ____O S____
9. ____F E____
10. ____M D____
11. ____A I____
12. ____R E____
13. ____C H____
14. ____H T____

THE LONG WORD WINS!

Find the *longest possible* word that can be spelled from the letters in each of the words below. Score as many points for each word as it has letters. Example: 1. Obtain the word SLUTS from the word TUSSLE and score 5 points for it. In some instances you will be able to make a word longer than the answer provided. PAR SCORE is 103 points.

1. _____TUSSLE
2. _____HATCHET
3. _____EMANATE
4. _____INNARDS
5. _____DILATION
6. _____ENSILAGE
7. _____STATEMENT
8. _____OBLIVIOUS
9. _____FEMININITY
10. _____MENDACIOUS
11. _____ADMIRATIONS
12. _____RESPONSIBLY
13. _____CALUMNIATING
14. _____HETERONYMOUS

RELATION'SHIPS'

Which ship would you say is the longest?

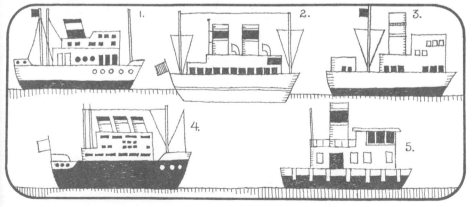

37

NO TELLING THROUGH SPELLING

This is a quiz about tricky words which, though spelled alike, are pronounced differently in order to express their exact meanings. In each
instance supply one such word for the correct completion of each
sentence below. A score of 7 and over is very good.

1. Though his legs seemed to feel like _____ the champion sprinter
   took an early _____ .
2. To see an actress in _____ on the screen _____ at the heart of
   most viewers.
3. The swimmer _____ into the pool on the edge of which a _____
   was sitting.
4. The _____ of the elephants to the rhythm of the band music did
   _____ the audience.
5. The doctor _____ a bandage around the injured part to protect
   the _____ .
6. The old employee had to _____ himself to the chairman in order
   to accept his _____ for long service.
7. Some visitors at the gallery _____ to the _____ shown there.
8. The chieftain with a _____ in his hand accepted the _____ of one
   of his tribesmen.

MIRROR MAGIC

This picture dates back to great-grandparents' time. Try to determine
at first glance how many different persons can be seen in this illustration.

HOW'S YOUR PLURALITY?

To spell a word is one thing. To spell the correct plural of many words is definitely another. Can you, for instance, spell the plurals of such simple words as NOTARY PUBLIC or POTATO without flinching? Well, here is a chance for you to find out for yourself to what extent plurals nonplus you. Get a comfortable plurality of 40 or more, and right here and now, you will have accomplished one of your CHEF*S* D'OEUVRE.

1. Thesis
2. Aide-de-camp
3. Spokesman
4. Notary public
5. Château
6. Franc-tireur
7. Sheaf
8. Court-martial
9. Moose
10. Table d'hôte
11. Opossum
12. Coco
13. Enigma
14. Attorney general
15. Rabbi
16. Fez

17. Governor general
18. Odeum
19. Ox
20. Bantu
21. Onyx
22. Judge Advocate
23. John Dory
24. Gentlemen's gentleman
25. Jack-in-the-box
26. Hors d'oeuvre
27. Sheath
28. Talisman
27. Potato
30. Brigadier general
31. Species
32. Son-in-law

33. Fife
34. Genus
35. Finnan haddie
36. Jinnee
37. Man-of-war
38. Auto-da-fé
39. If
40. Cousin-german
41. Papyrus
42. Norman
43. Mongoose
44. Musk deer
45. Hundredweight
46. Ignis fatuus
47. Handful
48. Infant prodigy

HIDDEN WORDS

Add and subtract the letters in the names of pictures shown below. If your answers are correct, in each case, you are in for a tasty surprise.

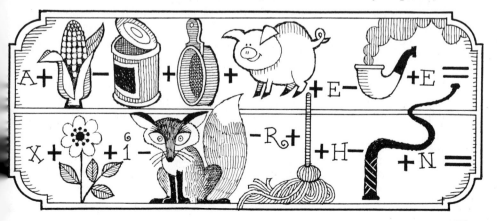

39

DEFINITIONS AND DICTIONARIES

Here is a simple game that will provide endless hours of varied entertainment. All that is needed to play is a dictionary, paper and pencils, and a vivid imagination. The object of the game is to fool your opponents through your ability to fabricate definitions to words that none of you know.

HOW TO PLAY

1. Each player takes a pencil and sheet of paper, numbering the paper from one to five. Any number of people can play.
2. One player acts as the moderator for the first round and takes up the dictionary. He scans through it hunting for 5 words that none of the players know the meaning of. If he does pick one that someone knows, then he should find another word.

Next he pronounces and spells each word out loud, writing the correct definition for each on his own sheet of paper. (Abbreviated definitions may be used for a faster game and should be used when playing with younger children, who will have trouble using the technical language required in a dictionary.) Even though there is more than one definition for a given word, use only one definition.
3. The other players write down the five words and then think up a definition for each which they feel will sound valid. The idea is to fabricate a definition that other players will accept as the most likely one. When each player has written his five fake definitions he signs his paper and passes it to the moderator.
4. When the moderator has collected all the sheets of paper he adds his sheet with the correct definitions and shuffles them. He then reads all the definitions for the first word (including the correct one).

Each player then tries to guess which definition is the proper one. The moderator keeps a record of the guesses on his paper.

The papers are then reshuffled and the process is repeated with the second word. When all five words have been covered in this fashion the

moderator tallies the scores and passes the dictionary to the next player who will serve as moderator for the next round.

After each player has had his turn as moderator the game is finished. The player with the highest score is the winner.

SCORING

If a player guesses the correct definition he scores one point. If another player is fooled and guesses a false definition, the player receives two points for *each* opponent he fools. A player *cannot* score points on the round which he serves as moderator.

Below is an example of the results of how one word might be scored.

Player A guessed the correct definition.
Player B guessed player E's definition.
Player C guessed player D's definition.
Player D guessed player E's definition.
Player E guessed the correct definition.

Player A receives one point for picking the correct definition.
Player B receives zero points. He guessed the wrong definition and no one picked his.
Player C receives zero points. Same reason as player B.
Player D receives two points. He guessed the wrong definition, but someone chose his.
Player E receives five points. He chose the correct definition plus two points each for the other players who picked his definition.

SPOT THE ODD ONES!

In each of the sets of 4 pictures below there is one picture that—logically —is entirely out of step with the other 3 pictures. Example: The figure 1C is the only one with an even number of sides. You won't be the odd-man-out with a score of 6 or more correct.

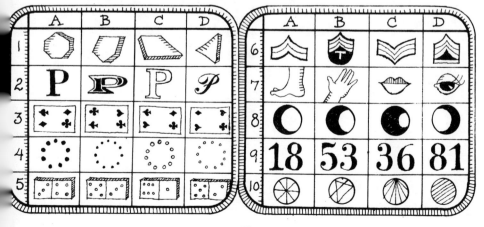

41

OH, THESE ANACHRONISTIC ARTISTS!

In attempting to depict a scene from ancient Greece, our prop man has made enough mistakes to warrant expulsion by any union. There are actually 23 errors by our count. You will do well to find 15; find all, and you qualify as chief prop man.

HOW QUICK-WITTED ARE YOU?

1. STRANGE EQUATION

If you *deduct* the number 5 from a certain number and divide the result into 4, you will receive a two-digit number. But you will receive the same two-digit number when you *add* 5 to the basic figure and divide the result into 5. Can you tell the basic number?

2. HOW REFLECTIVE ARE YOU

An eyewitness in court was asked about the exact time of an accident. He said: "From my window I look upon a street; my apartment is above a barbershop, the clock of which is reflected in a store window opposite my house. When I looked at that clock its hands appeared to indicate that it was 20 minutes after 5 o'clock when I heard the crash. The barber's clock usually is 10 minutes slow, so that the time of the accident was exactly _____." Our eyewitness was interrupted at this point by the judge, who ruled that the information was sufficient for accurately determining the time of the accident. What time did the eyewitness give?

3. A WEIGHTY WOMAN

A woman works in a candy store in Chicago. Her measurements are 36–24–36, and she is 5′5″ tall and wears size 9 shoes. What would she weigh?

4. WHOSE MOVE IS IT?

Messrs. WALKER, RUNNER, RIDER, and HIKER are walking, running, riding, and hiking. None of the four is doing the thing his name suggests. Neither Mr. RUNNER nor Mr. RIDER is walking. The hiker is not Mr. WALKER, and the runner is not Mr. RIDER. Can you tell how each man is moving?

5. CHANGE YOUR PARTNERS

Only three people in this group of men and women have moved so that the order as shown in the lower diagram results. Can you tell which people moved to which places?

```
        W
      W   M
    M   W   M
  M   W   M   W

  M   W   M   W
    M   W   M
      W   M
        W
```

ANIMAL HUNT IN CITIES

Contained in the name of each of the cities to be guessed is the name of an animal, more fully described in the definition. The length of each city's name is indicated by dots and dashes (on the left). The dashes represent the number of letters used to designate the particular animal indicated in the definition that follows the dots and dashes. Example: 1) AtlANTa. How many animals can you trap in their cities? A score of 16 or more and you qualify as a big game hunter.

1) . . . . _ _ .   busy insect in a Southern capital
2) _ _ . . . .   bovine in an English university town
3) . . _ _ _ .   fowl in a Greek city
4) . _ _ _ _ . . .   amphibian in a Dutch city
5) . . . . _ _ _ _ _ _   kind of antelope in a city on Lake Erie
6) . . . _ _ _   bovine in a Russian city
7) _ _ _ _ .   bird in an English coastal city
8) . . . . _ _ . .   monkey in a Hungarian city
9) . . . . _ _ . . equine in a Southern capital
10) . _ _ _ _   sea eagle in Switzerland
11) _ _ _ _ .   fatal reptile in a Western resort
12) _ _ _ . . . . .   quadruped female in Syria
13) _ _ _ .   long fish in a Midwestern city
14) _ _ _ _ . .   amphibian in a New England town
15) . . . _ _ _   serpent in a Panama town
16) _ _ _ . . .   Tibetan bovine in a Washington city
17) _ _ _ . . . .   deer in a Midwestern city
18) . . . . _ _ .   diving bird in a Wisconsin city
19) . . . _ _ . . .   slippery fish in a West Virginia city
20) . . . . _ _ . . .   battering quadruped in a Western capital

A SQUARE PROBLEM

How many black tiles and how many white tiles are needed to fill out the tileless part in the center of the floor?

WHAT GOES ON IN THE LETTER CIRCLE?

For directions on solving this puzzle, please turn to page 17.

FOR YOUNGSTERS	FOR PARENTS
A) Total	A) Roman statesman
B) Great German composer	B) Composer and organist
C) Part of face	C) Place of exile
D) Pain	D) Mapmaker
E) Patrick _____: Patriot	E) Elizabeth
F) Color	F) Applicant's statement
G) Article	G) "Liberty or death" man
H) English poetess	H) Mal de _____
I) Fowl	I) Poet's eye
J) Quarrel	J) Man of theses
K) Possess	K) Dusky
L) Period of history	L) American artist
M) Be excited about	M) Spiteful woman
N) That girl	N) Woman of the party
O) Feline	O) Bolero man
P) Sphere	P) Goddess
Q) That boy	Q) _____ Maria
R) Before	R) Long
S) German reformer	S) High or low
T) Beehive State: Abbr.	T) Conceding
U) Case of I	U) Christian or Byzantine
V) Either _____	V) Babylonian region
W) Satisfy fully	W) Whole
X) Hail!	X) Line
Y) Maurice _____: Composer	Y) _____ Mabel
Z) Take up again	Z) Large amount

45

FAMILY QUIZ GAME

For directions to this popular *Parents' Magazine* FAMILY QUIZ GAME, please turn to page 18.

FOR MOTHERS:

HOME ECONOMICS

(1) How many tablespoons equal a cup? (2) Does the dark or the white meat of chickens contain more vitamins? (3) What does antipasto mean literally? (4) Olive oil comes from olives but linseed oil comes from _____. (5) What is a cluster of bananas called? (6) What does the Latin expression *caveat emptor* mean? (7) How many pints are there in a gallon? (8) How many fluid ounces in a liquid quart? (9) True or false? Oleomargarine has fewer calories than butter. (10) Is tarragon a spice or an herb?

FOR FATHERS:

LEADERS

(1) Marshal Tito and _____. (2) Who is the Chairman of the Communist Party in China? (3) Secretary U Thant of the United Nations is from what country? (4) Archbishop Makarios and _____. (5) With whom did Lincoln have his famous debates? (6) Who followed David Ben Gurion as Premier of Israel? (7) Who was Disraeli's greatest political rival? (8) What is Premier Ky's full name? (9) Name the first Harvard graduate to become President of the U.S. (10) Who was Prime Minister of Great Britain from 1945–1951?

FOR YOUNGSTERS (5–6 YEARS)

NURSERY RHYMES

(1) What was it that Jack Sprat could not eat? (2) Who kissed the girls and made them cry? (3) In the nursery rhyme, "Jack Be Nimble," what is Jack going to do? (4) In the rhyme, "Mary Had a Little Lamb," where does the lamb follow Mary? (5) Can you complete this rhyme: "Mary, Mary, quite contrary, how does _____?" (6) Where did Peter, Peter, Pumpkin-Eater put his wife? (7) What did Little Miss Muffet sit on? (8) When the cow jumped over the moon, what did the little dog do? (9) What did the Three Little Kittens lose? (10) In the rhyme, "This Little Pig," where did the first little pig go?

BIRDS

(1) The bird which is said to put its head into the sand is an _____ .
(2) What bird suggests happiness? (3) What bird suggests bad language?
(4) How did the catbird get its name? (5) Which flies faster, a humming-bird or a sparrow? (6) The bird that is the symbol of the U.S. is an
_____ . (7) What bird looks as if it were wearing a tuxedo? (8) What
bird uses its wings for swimming? (9) What is the largest bird in the
world? (10) Hummingbirds hum with their a. feet b. mouth c. wings.

FOR PRE-TEENS (10–12 YEARS)

CITIES

(1) True or false: Constantinople and Istanbul are two present-day cities.
(2) True or false: The divided city of Berlin is located on the border line
between East and West Germany. (3) Cheyenne is the capital of which
state? (4) In what city does the United Nations meet? (5) In what cities
are the following streets a. Wall Street b. Champs Elysées c. Unter den
Linden. (6) Name Boston's baseball stadium. (7) What Italian city uses
boats as buses? (8) What is the name of the town where the Wright
brothers flew their first successful airplane? (9) In what building and in
what city is the Liberty Bell located? (10) Where is the Eiffel Tower?

FOR YOUNG TEENS (13–15 YEARS)

FIGURING

(1) To have a Friday the 13th, the month must start on what day?
(2) How do you find the area of a rectangle? (3) The square root of .09 is
_____ . (4) How much is 2½ x 2½? (5) What is the total of a dozen plus
a score plus a gross? (6) What is .75% of $100? (7) If I apply a force of
50 lbs. for one minute against a 1000 lb. weight and I am unable to move
it, how much work have I done? (8) The tangent of 45° equals _____ .
(9) In moving the decimal point to the right two places, we multiply by
_____ . (10) Is the series 2, 5, 8, 11 an arithmetical or geometrical pro-
gression?

WHAT GOES WITH WHAT IN THE PICTURE CIRCLE?

Here you will find 20 objects, each of which can be associated with at least one other—though some may be associated with several other—pictures. (For example: The cow could be associated with MILK, BUTTER, or CHEESE.) However, in the end there must be only 10 pairs of pictures that belong together so that NONE IS LEFT UNMATCHED, and for this there is only one solution.

APRIL

CALENDAR OF MEMORABLE DATES

1 April Fools' Day

2

3 Pony Express began, Ap. 1860, ended, Oct. 1861

4 Dorothy Dix, 1802–87, pioneer in prison and asylum reform

Present design of flag adopted, 1818

5 Booker T. Washington, 1856–1915, Negro educator and leader

6 Adm. Peary reached the North Pole, 1909

7 William Wordsworth, 1770–1850, English poet

8 Ponce de Leon landed in Florida, 1513

Louisiana, 18th state, admitted, 1812

9 Nikolai Lenin, 1870–1924, leader of the Russian Revolution

Lee surrendered to Grant, 1865

10 U.S. Patent system established, 1790

Com. Perry, 1794–1858, opened Japan to Western world

11 Charles Evans Hughes, 1862–1948, Chief Justice, 1930–41

12 Bombardment of Fort Sumter, 1861

13 Edict of Nantes, 1598, granted religious freedom in France

Thomas Jefferson, 1743–1826, 3rd President

14 S.S. Titanic sank on maiden voyage, 1912

15

16 Anatole France, 1844–1924, French author and humanitarian

Charles Chaplin, 1889– famed movie comedian

17

18 Paul Revere's midnight ride, 1775

19 Battle of Lexington and Concord, marking start of American Revolution, 1775

20

21

22 Opening of Oklahoma Territory, 1889

23 William Shakespeare, 1564–1616

24 Library of Congress established, 1800

25

26 Confederate Memorial Day

27 U. S. Grant, 1822–85, 18th President

Samuel Morse, 1791–1872, invented telegraph and Morse code

28 James Monroe, 1758–1831, 5th President

Maryland ratified Constitution, 1788

29 Arthur Wellesley, Duke of Wellington, 1769–1852, Defeated Napoleon at Waterloo

30 Washington inaugurated, 1789

49

CLASSIFIED NONSENSE

April Fool's Day suggests a game of the absurd, a game that should bring the sharpest mind to the fore quickly. One member of the party reads one or more of the following statements aloud while everybody is challenged to unmask the one absurdity contained in the statement as fast as possible. Nail down 10 or more instances of pure nonsense, with sound reasoning of your own, and you prove that you're nobody's fool.

1. COLLECTOR'S ITEM
A cornerstone just found in Rome dating from the time of Julius Caesar. It bears the date LXI B.C.

2. FOR SALE
A shrunken head from the head hunting Jivaro tribe, which a movie expedition just brought back from a hunting trip to East Africa.

3. ATTENTION, CURATORS
Bids will be received for the binoculars with which Columbus took his first look at the New World.

4. FOR EPITAPH COLLECTORS
A curious epitaph just discovered is the following:
"Owen Moore has run away
Owin more than he could pay"
b. April 6, 1830   d. Feb. 29, 1894

5. UNIQUE OPPORTUNITY
The tripod on which Newton had been sitting watching the famous apple fall will be auctioned off shortly. Though wobbly, it is still in good condition.

6. SEEKERS OF TRUTH
"I claim that no general statement is always true!"
Write to OLD PHILOSOPHER

7. COIN EXCHANGE
Wish to swap current Brazilian dollar for Mexican dollar of equal value.

8. BOOK MART
Want to sell beautiful old leather-bound Bible bearing this personal dedication: "To my best friend in devotion—George I, King of Great Britain."

9. MEMO TO LONDON-BOUND TRAVELERS
A favorite sight-seeing spot of Americans in London is the famous unique monument in honor of Sherlock Holmes, the founder of Scotland Yard.

10. MORE BOOK NEWS

The valuable first edition of Hamlet displayed at Auction House. It has two torn pages, 37 and 38, otherwise in good condition.

11. AMERICANA

Offered for sale is the famous smith of iron who has been standing on top of a New England church for generations; he is the smith that hits on his anvil every time he hears the clock strike the full hour.

12. ATTENTION PARTY PLANNERS

Don't forget that each year Christmas Day and New Year's Day fall upon the same day of the week!

13. ATTENTION EVERYBODY

It has come to the attention of the Secretary of Justice that some unscrupulous persons have greatly misused the services of this classified section by making untrue statements. Although remedial steps have been taken, your cooperation is requested.

COMPETITIVE WORD GAMES FOR ALL

THE SHORT WORD WINS!

Find the *shortest possible* word by adding as FEW letters as possible to *each* side of each letter pair. (No S-endings or proper nouns!) Example: 4. fISt. Score 1 point for each letter added, 10 points if you are unable to make up a word. In some instances you will be able to find a word shorter than the answer provided. PAR SCORE is 28 points.

1. ____A	Y____		7. ____O	O____	
2. ____P	A____		8. ____O	F____	
3. ____R	D____		9. ____L	L____	
4. ____I	S____		10. ____S	I ____	
5. ____L	L____		11. ____D	R____	
6. ____F	O____		12. ____A	P____	

THE LONG WORD WINS!

Find the *longest possible* word that can be spelled from the letters in each of the words below. Score as many points for each word as it has letters. Example: 1. Get the word BREAD from the word ABRADE and score 5 points for it. In some instances you will be able to make a word longer than the answer provided. PAR SCORE is 84 points.

1. _____ABRADE	7. _____OBEDIENCE	
2. _____PRAISE	8. _____OSCILLATE	
3. _____RAREBIT	9. _____LENGTHWISE	
4. _____INGRATE	10. _____STRIDULATE	
5. _____LICENSEE	11. _____DOCTRINATES	
6. _____FRAGRANT	12. _____ASTROLOGIAN	

WHAT'S IN A NAME?

The names of a number of famous persons have entered the dictionary and become words of very definite meanings. Each of the sentences below gives you two clues, one referring to the personality and the other to the thing named after him or her. The answer to 1. is SANDWICH, which was so named after the EARL OF SANDWICH. Identify 15 or more for a good score.

1. What EARL can butter and bite into himself?
2. What horse-loving LORD can don and doff himself?
3. What CONQUEROR can choose himself as a tasty dessert?
4. What English GENERAL can step out in himself?
5. What ACTRESS can save herself with herself?
6. What famous RIFLESHOT can show herself and get to see a show for free?
7. What Scottish ENGINEER can build a road with himself?
8. What American OFFICER can shoot at the enemy with himself?
9. What Flemish ARTIST can sport himself on the chin?
10. What MANUFACTURER can rest or write on himself?
11. What French ARCHITECT can dwell in himself?
12. What MARQUISE can wear herself as a hair-do?
13. What American COLONEL can cut game with himself?
14. What MATHEMATICIAN can figure out subdivisions on himself?
15. What English WOMAN can eat herself at teatime?
16. What English CLERGYMAN can take a pleasure ride in himself?
17. What PRIME MINISTER can carry his belongings in himself?
18. What German INVENTOR can generate power by himself?
19. What French POLITICIAN can outline himself with himself?
20. What INVENTOR can tap a message with himself?

WHAT'S IN THE LETTER CLOSET?

Concealed in the letter maze are at least 22 items of wearing apparel. Move horizontally, vertically, or diagonally and repeat letters as often as necessary to spell out the name of the apparel. Example: Start at B in the top line, move to O, down to the next O, then to T, and get BOOT. A score of 15 or more is very good.

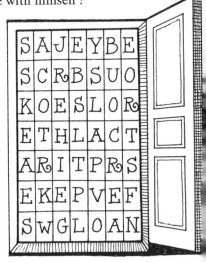

```
S A J E Y B E
S C R B S U O
K O E S L O R
E T H L A C T
A R I T P R S
E K E P V E F
S W G L O A N
```

TEST YOUR RELATIVITY!

Every school child learns at some time that President John Adams was the father of President John Quincy Adams. BUT could you tell with similar ease that the famous historian Henry Adams was John Quincy Adams's grandson? Your task here is to find out what relationship—if any—exists between each of the two famous people bearing the same name listed below. You are a clever person if you nail down 18 or more relationships (or non-relationships) correctly.

WHAT RELATIONSHIP EXISTS BETWEEN . . .

1. Franklin Roosevelt   and   Theodore Roosevelt?
2. Lyman Beecher   "   Harriet Beecher?
3. Herbert Hoover   "   J. Edgar Hoover?
4. Robert E. Lee   "   Henry Lee?
5. Fred Astaire   "   Adele Astaire?
6. Maria Theresa   "   Marie Antoinette?
7. William Booth   "   Ballington Booth?
8. Theodore Roosevelt   "   Eleanor Roosevelt?
9. Johns Hopkins   "   Mark Hopkins?
10. Raymond Massey   "   Ilona Massey?
11. William Taft   "   Robert Taft?
12. Charlotte Brontë   "   Emily Brontë?
13. George II   "   George III?
14. Otis Skinner   "   Cornelia Otis Skinner?
15. Catherine I   "   Catherine II?
16. Lionel Barrymore   "   Ethel Barrymore?
17. Horace Mann   "   Thomas Mann?
18. Amos Bronson Alcott   "   Louisa May Alcott?
19. Robert Scott   "   Walter Scott?
20. Sir John Herschel   "   Sir William Herschel
21. Daniel Webster   "   Noah Webster?
22. William H. Harrison   "   Benjamin Harrison?
23. Johann Strauss   "   Richard Strauss?
24. Louis XVI   "   Louis XVIII?
25. Austen Chamberlain   "   Neville Chamberlain?

FUN WITH MILK CARTONS

If you throw away a milk container after using it, you're missing a lot of excitement. They're valuable, so start saving them right now. Here are three milk-carton games. Try them!

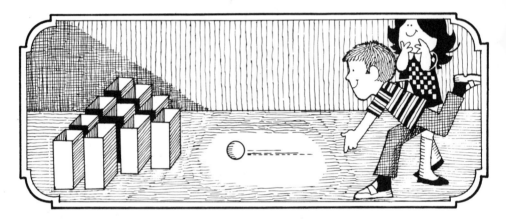

1. SET 'EM UP FOR BOWLING

Use empty quart size milk cartons as pins (you'll need 10 of them, so start saving them up for a rainy day) and a rubber ball. Almost any size rubber ball will do, but one about four inches in diameter is best. Set up the milk cartons in the shape of a triangle. Draw a line or stretch a cord across the floor, 10 feet from the cartons.

Then, from behind the line, roll the ball towards the cartons trying to knock them down. A "strike," knocking them all down at the first try, counts for 20 points. Each individual carton knocked down counts one point. When a player has rolled three times the pins are set up again and his opponent plays. The first player to make a score of 100 wins.

2. GOLF INDOORS

All you need for an indoor golf game are six or 12 milk cartons, a small ball for each player and toy golf clubs or umbrellas with curved handles.

Cut the tops off the milk cartons. Lay them on their sides in a semi-circle around the room using 12 if the room is large enough or six if it's smaller. Number them from one to 12, or one to six.

Each player stands in the middle of the semi-circle and tries to hit the ball into hole one. If it goes in, he tries for hole two, etc. As soon as he misses, his opponent begins. When the first player's turn comes around again, he starts with the hole he missed until all the players have successfully hit the ball into all the holes. The one who has taken the least amount of strokes wins.

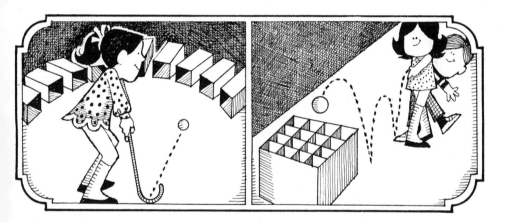

3. BOUNCE BALL

Here's another way to have fun with empty milk cartons. Use five cartons, cutting each of them in half so that you have ten "cups." Place them, open ends up, in a box large enough to hold all 10 of them. Mark the 10 cups in this way: 5, 10, 15, 20, 25, 30, 35, 40, 45, 50. Now use any small ball that has a good bounce. The idea of the game is for one player to bounce the ball on the floor once and then into one of the cups. His score is the number on the cup into which the ball goes. First player to earn a total score of 500 wins the game.

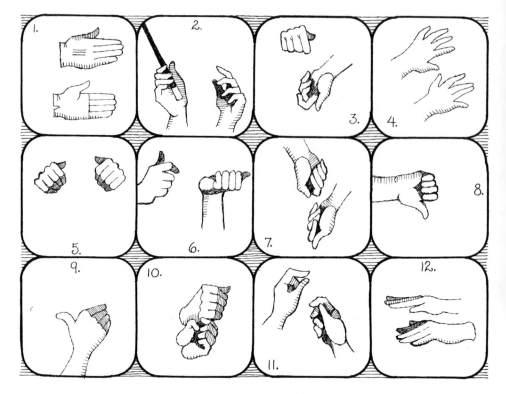

NICE 'HAND'IWORK IF YOU CAN GET IT

Can you understand the "language of hands" by attributing to each picture the profession or the activity of the owner for each pair of hands shown above? You are a HANDY sleuth if you spot 8 or more professions or activities correctly.

BIG GAME HUNTING

Without counting, tell which of the animals has the greatest number of hunters (depicted as dots) following it?

RIDDLES, RIDDLES, RIDDLES

1. Why are bald men always so cheerful?
2. Can you name the capital of all the states in one minute?
3. What do the neighbors of a horn player do that his fingers do?
4. Why doesn't a thief worry?
5. What does a baseball team have in common with a set of dishes?
6. What is a bull called when he's sleeping?
7. Which 50 coins add up to a dollar?
8. Why did the little boy take sugar and cream to the movies?
9. Why would a lazy housewife rather wash a mirror than a window?
10. Why did the little boy sleep on the chandelier?
11. What is the quietest game in the world?
12. What's worse than a giraffe with a sore throat?
13. What gadget do we use to see through a wall?
14. Why did the rabbit go over the hill?
15. How can you raise corn beef and cabbage?
16. What did Benjamin Franklin say when he discovered electricity?
17. If you took two apples, three peaches, and ten grapes what would you have?
18. Why was the library sad?
19. The stagecoach arrived in town without wheels; what held it up?
20. What is a buccaneer?
21. My first syllable is a farm animal, my second is the end of it, and my whole is something that girls wear. What am I?
22. Why did the three little pigs leave home?

HOW'S YOUR GENERAL STORE OF INFORMATION?

There are over 20 items to be had in this store. How many can you find?
A score of 20 is very good, if you find 26 you are tops!

WHAT GOES ON IN THE LETTER CIRCLE?

For an explanation of how best to solve this puzzle, please turn to page 17.

FOR YOUNGSTERS

A) Make a mistake
B) Discovered North Pole
C) Part of head
D) Russian communist leader
E) A malicious look
F) Small bird
G) Surrendered to Grant
H) Brown
 I) Mature
J) Beer
K) Ship of disaster fame
L) Ring a bell
M) Fruit
N) Dessert
O) Midnight rider
P) Vegetable
Q) Columbus' ship
R) Before
S) Greek deity
T) More pleasing
U) Tear
V) Toward the sheltered side
W) Stake
X) Adam's wife
Y) Insect
Z) French city

FOR PARENTS

A) Pay
B) Nikolai
C) French edict city
D) Attention
E) Special perception
F) American painter
G) Disaster ship
H) Yours _____
 I) Black bird
J) Small bird
K) Discoverer
L) Ring
M) Elihu
N) Riviera place
O) Bakery man
P) Cronus or Rhea
Q) Beach color
R) Noted orator
S) Lascivious glance
T) Bar item
U) Surrenderer
V) Christopher's ship
W) Transgress
X) French dream
Y) Strike violently
Z) Marble

59

FAMILY QUIZ GAME

For an introduction to this popular *Parents' Magazine* FAMILY QUIZ GAME please turn to page 18.

FOR MOTHERS:
MEDICINE

(1) A dermatologist is concerned primarily with diseases of the a. skin b. heart c. lungs. (2) Whose oath do all physicians take? (3) Are all bacteria harmful? (4) Hepatitis is a disease of the a. heart b. liver c. lungs. (5) With what medical specialty is Karl Menninger associated? (6) A doctor who specializes in the diseases of the bones and joints is called an _____. (7) Does a placebo contain medicine? (8) If you suffer from acrophobia you have a fear of _____. (9) What is a sphygmomanometer used for? (10) The ill-functioning of what organ usually causes diabetes?

FOR FATHERS:
SPORTS

(1) _____ was the first black man to win the heavyweight boxing championship. (2) True or false: The Olympic games were originally held by the Romans. (3) How many home runs did Babe Ruth hit in his record making year, 1927? (4) What baseball player was known as "The Pride of St. Louis"? (5) In golf, the term _____ indicates one under par. (6) What prizefighter was known as the Manassa Mauler? (7) What baseball player was known as the Iron Horse? (8) In ice hockey the object the players hit with a stick is called a _____. (9) What football player was known as the "Galloping Ghost"? (10) In trap shooting, _____ are the objects shot at.

FOR YOUNGSTERS (5–6 YEARS)
FOOD

(1) Pork comes from a. cow b. lamb c. fish d. pig. (2) True or false: Butter is made from cream. (3) Are pretzels salty or sweet? (4) What shape is an orange? (5) Is a banana a fruit or a vegetable? (6) True or false: Horses do not eat meat. (7) What color is the skin of a grapefruit? (8) Who ate curds and whey? (9) What did little Jack Horner eat? (10) From what two states do oranges mainly come?

FOR JUNIORS (6½–9 YEARS)

THE SEA

(1) Name the two largest oceans. (2) Name the large body of water that touches Northern Mexico, Florida, and Texas. (3) A group of fish is called a _____. (4) Do bony fish sleep with their eyes open? (5) Do sea horses live on land or in water? (6) Are ocean tides controlled to a greater degree by the sun or the moon? (7) What is the name of a body of land completely surrounded by water? (8) Is the North Pole located in the Arctic or in the Antarctic? (9) True or false: The Marines fight on the sea only. (10) True or false: Approximately three fourths of the earth's surface is covered by water.

FOR PRE-TEENS (10–12 YEARS)

THE BIBLE

(1) Name the Old Testament character who was sold into slavery by his older brothers. (2) The wisest King of Israel in the Old Testament was _____. (3) The character in the Old Testament whose strength depended on his hair never being cut was _____. (4) Name the Old Testament figure that led the Israelites out of Egypt. (5) What Jewish holiday commemorates the event in number four? (6) The queen of what country paid a visit to Solomon? (7) On what mountain peak were the Ten Commandments given? (8) What was on the ladder which Jacob saw? (9) What was the final plague that made Pharaoh let the Israelites go? (10) Who caused the sun to stand still?

FOR YOUNG TEENS (13–15 YEARS)

MEANINGS

(1) What is a palindrome? (2) Arch, cantilever, and suspension describe types of _____. (3) When you bury the hatchet you a. start a quarrel b. end a quarrel. (4) What does the motto of the Marines *Semper Fidelis* mean? (5) What word can mean both an English king and a coin? (6) Explain gerrymandering. (7) What does ambivalence mean? (8) True or false: Semantics is the study of meanings and their relation to the words which represent them in language. (9) What does the Latin phrase *cum laude* mean? (10) What does automobile mean literally?

A CUBIST'S DELIGHT

Count the number of blocks in each pile. You must include the hidden blocks necessary to support those that are shown. Get them all correct and you qualify as cubist of the year.

❋ CALENDAR OF MEMORABLE DATES

1 May Day	**2** Leonardo DaVinci, died 1519, "Genius of the Renaissance" Catherine the Great, 1729–96, of Russia	**3** Machiavelli, 1469–1527, Florentine statesman	**4** Horace Mann, 1796–1859, pioneer American educator Thomas Huxley, 1825–95, English biologist
5 Arbor Day	**6**	**7** Robert Browning, 1812–89, noted English poet	**8** Jean Dunant, 1828–1910, founded Red Cross Harry S. Truman, 1884– , 33rd President
9 John Brown, 1800–59, famed abolitionist	**10** Second meeting of Continental Congress in Philadelphia, 1775 Transcontinental R.R. completed, 1869	**11** Minnesota, 32nd state, admitted, 1858	**12** Florence Nightingale, 1820–1910, founder of modern nursing
13 Jamestown, Va., first English colony, 1607	**14**	**15** First regular air mail in the world, started in U.S. in 1918	**16**
17	**18**	**19**	**20** Dorothea (Dolly) Madison, 1768–1849, "First Lady" in the White House
21 Charles Lindbergh flew Atlantic, 1927 American Red Cross organized, 1881	**22**	**23** South Carolina ratified Constitution, 1788	**24** Queen Victoria, 1819–1901, English monarch
25 Ralph Waldo Emerson, 1803–82, outstanding American poet, essayist and lecturer	**26**	**27** Golden Gate Bridge opened, 1937	**28**
29 J. F. Kennedy, 1917–63, 35th President	**30** Memorial Day, commemorates U.S. war dead	**31** Walt Whitman, 1819–92, American poet, known as "The good gray poet"	

63

ARE YOU MOTHERWISE?

It's Mother's Day month, and off we go with 10 definitions for words that begin with the word MOTHER. If you are able to guess 8 or more of the words defined you are indeed motherwise.

1. Another name for the planet we live on.
2. A common way of referring to the country of origin of one's parents or ancestors.
3. The name of a fictitious teller of fairy tales.
4. A nickname for England.
5. A common name for one's first language.
6. A nickname for the state of Virginia.
7. A material favored by buttonmakers.
8. Name used for a type of loose, full gown.
9. The nun who is the head of a religious house.
10. A title used for Ayeshah, Mohammed's favorite wife.

DO YOU KNOW THEIR MOTHERS?

Do you know the words for the mothers of the dozen animals listed below? For instance: The mother of a tiger would be a TIGRESS. A score of 10 or over is very good.

1. Chicken
2. Piglet
3. Lamb
4. Lionet
5. Ass
6. Calf
7. Horse
8. Fox
9. Kitten
10. Goat
11. Fallow deer
12. Red deer

MA'S WITHOUT SONS

The words to be guessed for the score of definitions listed below all end in MA. How many can you find? A score of 16 or more entitles you to a diploMA."

1. Fragrance
2. Hat
3. Maxim
4. Greek letter
5. Greek letter
6. Brand
7. The fluid part of blood
8. Molten rock
9. Complete view
10. Noxious exhalation
11. Tibetan Buddhist Monk
12. Theatrical play
13. Motion pictures
14. Grammatical mark
15. Mental shock
16. Torpor
17. Riddle
18. Greek coin
19. State
20. Perplexing situation

COMPETITIVE WORD GAMES FOR ALL

THE SHORT WORD WINS!

Find the *shortest possible* word by adding as FEW letters as possible to *each* side of each letter pair. (No S-endings or proper nouns!) Example: 2. oPEn. Score 1 point for each letter added, 10 points if you can NOT make up a word. In some instances you will be able to find a word shorter than the answer provided. PAR SCORE is 30 points.

1. _____S R_____   6. _____G G_____
2. _____P E_____   7. _____F N_____
3. _____R V_____   8. _____E I_____
4. _____I E_____   9. _____V R_____
5. _____N F_____   10. _____E P_____

THE LONG WORD WINS!

Find the *longest possible* word that can be spelled from the letters in each of the words below. Score as many points for each word as it has letters. Example: 1. Get the word GHOULS from the word SLOUGH and score 6 points for it. In some instances you will be able to make a word longer than the answer provided. PAR SCORE is 69 points.

1. _____ SLOUGH   6. _____ GRADIENT
2. _____ PLANET   7. _____ FRUSTRATE
3. _____ RESIDUE   8. _____ ESTABLISH
4. _____ INWARDS   9. _____ VEGETATION
5. _____ NEBULOUS   10. _____ ENTHUSIASM

LOONEY LOGIC   This man sold 7 balloons altogether, but, at some point replenished his stock—the little girl did not buy the last of the sold balloons—put the pictures into their logical order and tell which balloon was sold last.

65

DAMSEL IN DISTRESS

Help the Knight rescue the beautiful Princess, but beware the hungry dragon!

FLOWERY ANSWERS

Each of the following clues somehow suggests the name of a flower. For example, "One hour before teatime" would be FOUR-O'CLOCK. A score of 15 or more flowery answers is very good.

1. Distressingly pleasing
2. Infant's respiration
3. Confine a forest
4. Think of me always
5. Distinction at dawn
6. Bovine petticoat
7. Keeps Reynard's hands warm
8. Misogynist's knob
9. Cover mug with fat
10. Rooster's adornment
11. John in an elevated church place
12. Singing bird, hasten!
13. Break, fabled animal!
14. Melancholy ring
15. Allot ourselves
16. Beloved Bill
17. Wearing indefinitely
18. Core's comfort
19. Auto-conscious people
20. Sitting this one out

FLOWER BRIDGE

The words listed in the numbered columns at the left can be linked with the words listed in the alphabetical columns at the right, so that a well-known flower will result—PROVIDED you also find the missing one-letter-bridge between the two words. Example: Link 1. MAR with (e) GOLD for MAR I GOLD. You will deserve a real bouquet with a score of 15 or more flowers found in 5 minutes.

1. MAR	11. LO	(a) HID	(k) CLOCK
2. EVE	12. SNOW	(b) ALL	(l) ELL
3. COW	13. TUB	(c) HORN	(m) MILE
4. FOUR	14. DO	(d) IS	(n) CUP
5. FLY	15. COCK	(e) GOLD	(o) US
6. BUTTE	16. DROP	(f) WOOD	(p) LOWER
7. HARE	17. I	(g) ROSE	(q) COMB
8. HAW	18. MONK	(h) LIP	(r) RAP
9. FOX	19. CAM	(i) LASTING	(s) LOVE
10. OR	20. SUN	(j) ORT	(t) HOOD

THE MAGIC KEY

How would you like to fool your friends with a mind reading trick so mystifying that even you won't know how you do it? Just read the instructions below and follow them carefully.

WHAT YOU DO: Note the picture of a key with five different geometrical symbols along its stem. Ask your friend to put his finger on any one of these five designs. As soon as he does so, turn your back so you can't see the page. While your back is turned, tell him to:

1. Close his eyes and think of a number above ten.

2. Start tapping symbols, moving up the key's stem and counting silently with each tap. After he reaches the star on the circle, he may turn either right or left, and continue counting. Just to illustrate: Let's suppose your friend chooses the number 13 and has selected the second symbol from the bottom as his starting point. This symbol counts for one as he begins counting. He continues counting up the stem and around the circle until he reaches number 13. (If it is a large number he may have to tap several times around the circle.)

3. Now he must count back *around the circle* in the *opposite* direction. The last symbol tapped also counts as 1. He keeps tapping around the circle until he reaches number 13 again. Then he stops and looks at the symbol his finger is touching. He concentrates his deepest thoughts on this design.

While he is thinking, you rub your temples and pretend you are receiving his "thought waves." Then you calmly tell him the symbol he is thinking of!

Remember—your back is turned until you name the symbol. He does not tell you the number he used, and you should make sure that he does all his counting silently so you will have no clue concerning the design on which his count finally ends. There seems to be no way you could name the design correctly except by reading his mind!

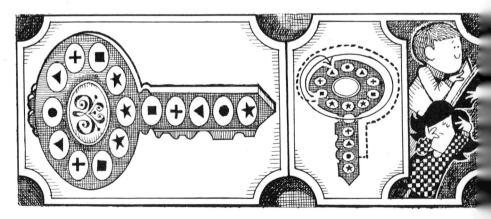

HOW YOU DO IT: At the beginning of the trick, when he first puts his finger on a symbol, note the design immediately *above* it, this will be the symbol on which his last count will end, no matter what number he chooses!

THE GREAT CARD MYSTERY

This amazing trick will really baffle your friends. Here's what happens: The magician riffles a deck of cards. All the cards show black. Then he commands the deck to change color and riffles it again. Magically, the cards have turned red! Here's how this marvelous feat is performed.

MATERIALS NEEDED: A deck of cards and a pair of scissors. Use an old deck that no one will care to play with again, or buy an inexpensive deck.

WHAT YOU DO: With the scissors trim about 1/16th of an inch from one edge of every black card in the deck (see picture #1). Do this as neatly as you can.

Now arrange the deck so that the black and red cards alternate—first a red card, then a black, and so on (see picture #2). Put the Joker on the bottom of the pack, and you're ready to do the trick.

HOW IT'S DONE: First, tap the deck on the table, as shown in picture #3. This is to make sure that all the "short" cards are flush with the lower end of the pack.

Next, hold the deck with your right hand exactly as shown in picture #4. Flip the top ends of the cards with your left thumb. All the cards will appear to be black!

Wave your hand over the deck and command it to change color (see picture #5). Now hold the lower end of the deck in your *left* hand (see picture #6) and flip the top ends of the cards with your *right* fingers in the manner shown. All the cards will have mysteriously changed to red!

After you have made the deck change color several times, be sure to put the cards away so no one can examine the deck and discover its secret construction!

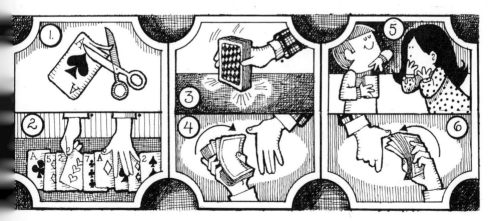

WHAT'S THE GAME?

The diagrams pictured here (not to scale) give you a bird's-eye view of the layouts of the courts or fields of different games. Even if you are not a fan of all the games represented, you will probably be able to recognize most of them by name. With a score of 12 or more you have played your GAME OF GAMES very well.

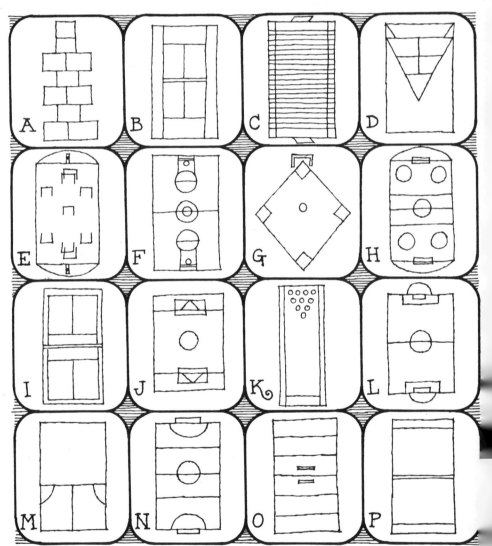

SCRAMBLED CALLING CARDS

Re-arrange all the letters on the incomplete calling cards shown here and find out what the professions of the people named on the respective cards are. Name 6 or more and you qualify to carry card No. 5!

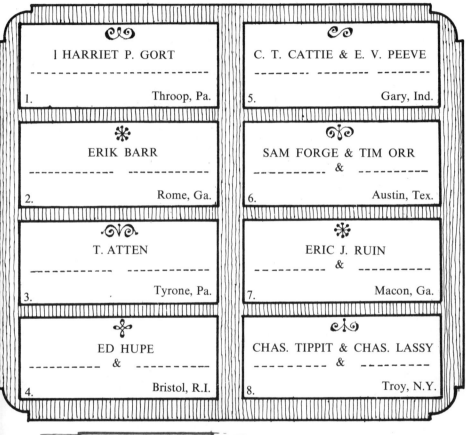

❧	❧
1 HARRIET P. GORT	C. T. CATTIE & E. V. PEEVE
--------------------------	-------- -------- --------
1. Throop, Pa.	5. Gary, Ind.
✳	❧
ERIK BARR	SAM FORGE & TIM ORR
------------- -----------	---------- & ----------
2. Rome, Ga.	6. Austin, Tex.
❧	✳
T. ATTEN	ERIC J. RUIN
------------ -----------	---------- & ----------
3. Tyrone, Pa.	7. Macon, Ga.
❧	❧
ED HUPE	CHAS. TIPPIT & CHAS. LASSY
--------- & ----------	--------- & --------
4. Bristol, R.I.	8. Troy, N.Y.

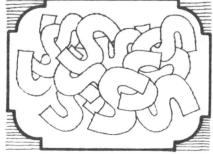

AN 'ESS'ENTIAL PROBLEM

How many S's can you see here, interwoven as they are?

WHERE WOULD YOU MEET THESE PEOPLE?

Imagine yourself at the United Nations welcoming people from many countries. If you can tell the native land of at least 13 of the people below, you are indeed a man of the world.

1.) Maori
2.) Inca
3.) Moro
4.) Navaho
5.) Tungus
6.) Aztec
7.) Kabyle
8.) Fleming
9.) Papuan
10.) Tartar
11.) Singhalese
12.) Manchu
13.) Kanaka
14.) Magyar
15.) Swahili
16.) Dyak
17.) Turkoman
18.) Araucanian
19.) Lapp
20.) Amhara

THE NUMBER GAME

Try to execute the arithmetical operations here: like symbols—like numbers!

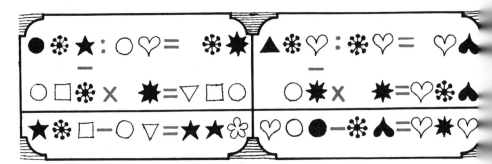

WHAT GOES ON IN THE LETTER CIRCLE?

For an explanation of how best to solve this puzzle, please turn to page 17.

FOR YOUNGSTERS

A) Individual
B) President
C) Tan
D) English poet
E) Stitch
F) Lair
G) _____ Gate Bridge
H) Alaska city
I) Alaska purchaser
J) Cry
K) Alcoholic beverage
L) Foundation
M) Kind of toast
N) Of yore
O) Napoleon's island
P) Aged
Q) Harass
R) Hair over eye
S) Hospital section
T) International organization
U) Conflict
V) _____ Domini
W) Have
X) American educator
Y) Quarrel
Z) Ask for payment

FOR PARENTS

A) Nellie _____ : Soprano
B) Kind of sister
C) Robert or Elizabeth
D) _____ Gate
E) Sinus cavity
F) Effrontery
G) Alaska peninsula
H) City on above
I) In _____ days
J) Horace
K) Father's retreat
L) _____ standard
M) Red Cross founder
N) Sepia or mahogany
O) Harry
P) Harry
Q) Horse
R) _____ Domini
S) Island
T) Stitch
U) Conflagration
V) Spat
W) Poor
X) _____ Hickory
Y) Watch
Z) Acknowledge

73

FAMILY QUIZ GAME

For an introduction to this popular *Parents' Magazine* FAMILY QUIZ GAME please turn to page 18.

FOR MOTHERS:

NOVELS

(1) Who wrote *Tom Jones*? (2) Name the first American novelist to win the Nobel Prize. (3) On what novel by Dumas is the opera *La Traviata* based? (4) Name Françoise Sagan's first great success. (5) The rise of the Chinese peasant Wang Lung was described in Pearl Buck's novel _____ . (6) What novel is the character Mr. Bumble from? (7) The novel *War and Peace* deals with the invasion of Russia by _____ . (8) Who wrote the novelette *The Sacred Fount*? (9) Name Katherine Anne Porter's novel about an imaginary voyage. (10) The Joad family is important in what novel?

FOR FATHERS:

SPACE

(1) True or false: The earth is inside the Milky Way. (2) The aurora borealis is more commonly referred to as the _____ . (3) The name of the first camera-carrying spacecraft landing on the moon by the U.S. is _____ . (4) Name the rocket that launched our first satellite. (5) How many miles from the center of the earth is the center of the moon a. 91,000 b. 239,000 c. 729,000? (6) How many miles up does air drag cease and space begin? (7) What is an astronomical unit? (8) When the moon is at the point where it is farthest from the earth it is said to be at _____ . (9) Are comets mostly gaseous or solid? (10) Cape Kennedy, the U.S. space center, was previously called _____ .

FOR YOUNGSTERS (5–6 YEARS)

MUSIC

(1) Which is larger, an accordion or a harmonica? (2) What are the first and third notes on the scale? (3) Name the only tune that Tom, the Piper's son, could play. (4) Who called for "his fiddlers three"? (5) Which is louder, a whisper or a yell? (6) True or false: All birds sing. (7) Ballet dancers dance on their _____ . (8) True or false: Lullabies are most often sung in the morning. (9) What is larger, a violin or a cello? (10) What is the difference between a musician and a magician?

FOR JUNIORS (6½–9 YEARS)

FAMOUS PEOPLE

(1) Daniel Boone was a _____ . (2) What famous statesman flew a kite in a thunderstorm to show that lightning was composed of electricity? (3) Amy Lowell is famous as a. an actress b. a poet c. a tennis champ. (4) What is ex-President Eisenhower's first name? (5) How did John D. Rockefeller make his fortune? (6) What office in the United Nations does U Thant hold? (7) Who was governor of New Amsterdam? (8) Cleopatra was once the ruler of a. Egypt b. England c. India. (9) What historic river did Caesar cross? (10) Who was born first, Abraham Lincoln or George Washington?

FOR PRE-TEENS (10–12 YEARS)

MYTHOLOGY

(1) A Gorgon was a hideous woman with _____ for hair. (2) A centaur is a fabled animal, half man, half _____ . (3) Who was Zeus? (4) What Greek deity was said to support the heavens on his shoulders? (5) Who is the Roman god pictured wearing a winged hat and winged sandals? (6) _____ was the Greek goddess of the dawn. (7) Name the mythical winged boy who shoots people with arrows to make them fall in love. (8) Name the Knight of the Round Table who fell in love with Queen Guinevere. (9) Where was King Arthur's Court? (10) Who were the legendary founders of Rome?

FOR YOUNG TEENS (13–15 YEARS)

MINERALS

(1) What metal will flow without heating? (2) Why is the Rosetta stone famous? (3) True or false: Silver is a good conductor for electricity. (4) The most abundant metal found in the ground is _____ . (5) True or false: Gold is lighter than iron. (6) The chemical name of common table salt is _____ . (7) Why does a piece of metal feel colder than a piece of wood even if both are at the same temperature? (8) What king had the golden touch? (9) True or false: Iron is made from steel. (10) What material is used in the lead of pencils?

'PEST'OLOGICAL, ISN'T IT?

Our candid cameraman caught the 12 scenes depicted here. In what order would they have to be put to conform to the sequence of their original occurrence?

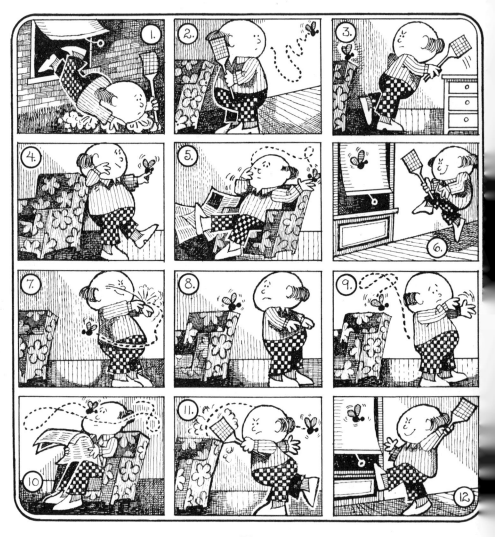

JUNE

CALENDAR OF MEMORABLE DATES

1 Brigham Young, 1801–77, American Mormon leader	**2**	**3** Jefferson Davis, 1808–89, Southern statesman, President of the Confederate States of America	**4** George III, 1738–1820, King of England at the time of the American Revolution.
5 First chapter of "Uncle Tom's Cabin" appeared in serial form, 1851.	**6** D-day, the Allied invasion of Europe, 1944	**7** Mohammed, the Prophet of Islam, died, 632	**8** Frank Lloyd Wright, 1869–1959, foremost American architect
9 Peter the Great, 1672–1725, Czar of Russia	**10**	**11** Richard Strauss, 1864–1949, German composer	**12**
13 Wm. Butler Yeats, 1865–1939, Irish dramatist and poet	**14** Flag Day	**15** Magna Charta signed by King John, 1215. Benjamin Franklin did famous kite experiment in 1752	**16**
17 Battle of Bunker Hill in Boston, 1775	**18** Father's Day	**19** Blaise Pascal, 1623–62, French scientist. H. L. (Lou) Gehrig, 1903–41, famed baseball player	**20** West Virginia, 35th state, admitted, 1863. Queen Victoria ascended English throne, 1837
21 Summer solstice, the first day of summer	**22**	**23** William Penn's treaty with the Indians, 1683	**24** Feast of St. John the Baptist
25 Custer's last stand at the Little Big Horn, 1876	**26**	**27** Helen Keller, 1880–1968, deaf and blind from infancy, famed writer	**28** Treaty of Versailles signed, ending WW I, 1919
29	**30** Senate voted statehood for Alaska, 1958. Yosemite Valley established as a public park, 1864		

IN FATHER'S FOOTSTEPS

What better tribute to Father's Day than to know about sons of distinguished fathers, in particular, sons who became as great as, or greater than, their fathers. Can you give the names of the ten brilliant sons described below? You are indeed an historian if you know 8 of them.

1. Who probably discovered America about A.D. 1000 after his father had discovered Greenland in 984?
2. What Biblical king, noted for his superior wisdom, whose very name has become a word for a "very wise man," was the son of another king, himself reigning for 40 years?
3. Who secured Florida for the United States while he was Secretary of State, being the only American who held this same high office as his father?
4. What noted composer outdid his father by composing almost 500 dance pieces and a number of operettas and became the most popular dance-orchestra conductor of the 19th century?
5. What author wrote *La Dame aux Camélias,* thus following the profession of his father, the most widely read storyteller of his time?
6. Who became Prime Minister of Britain at the age of twenty-four, and was again recalled to that post to form a coalition against Napoleon in 1805, thereby following his father, "the Great Commoner," who was also recalled in a time of need by George III?
7. What famous American preacher and lecturer, who influenced public opinion for the Union cause during an English lecture tour, had taken up the work of his father, a preacher and temperance advocate?
8. What famous American jurist—Chief Justice of the Supreme Court and author—was the son of another famous author, who originally was a practicing physician at Harvard?
9. What great military leader in the Civil War inherited the genius of his father, whose nickname was "Light-Horse Harry"?
10. Who was commander of the Salvation Army and later founded the Volunteers of America, thus continuing the work of his father, a religious leader who developed a London mission into the Salvation Army, of which he became the first general?

COMPETITIVE WORD GAMES FOR ALL

THE SHORT WORD WINS!

Find the *shortest possible* word by adding as FEW letters as possible to *each* side of each letter pair. (No S-endings or proper nouns!) Example: 2. sTAr. Score 1 point for each letter added, 10 points if you are unable to make up a word. In some instances you will be able to find a word shorter than the answer provided. PAR SCORE is 35 points.

1.	____S	Y____	7.	____H	H____
2.	____T	A____	8.	____I	T____
3.	____S	D____	9.	____N	I____
4.	____W	S____	10.	____S	W____
5.	____I	N____	11.	____D	S____
6.	____T	I____	12.	____A	T____

THE LONG WORD WINS!

Find the *longest possible* word that can be spelled from the letters in each of the words below. Score as many points for each word as it has letters. Example: 1. Get the word HIKERS from the word SHRIEK and score 6 points for it. In some instances you will be able to make a word longer than the answer provided. PAR SCORE is 89 points.

1.	_____SHRIEK	7.	_____INERTNESS
2.	_____THEIST	8.	_____NUMERATION
3.	_____WHEREAT	9.	_____STENTORIAN
4.	_____IDENTITY	10.	_____DEPRECIATED
5.	_____THRENODY	11.	_____AFTERTASTES
6.	_____HERBACIST	12.	_____YELLOWTHROAT

LET'S BUILD A HOUSE!

Concealed in the letter maze are at least 25 items that can be used in building a house. Move horizontally, vertically, or diagonally, and repeat letters as often as necessary to spell out the name of a building material. Example: Start at V, move to E, then to N, then double the E, and go to R and get VENEER. A score of 15 or more makes you a master-builder.

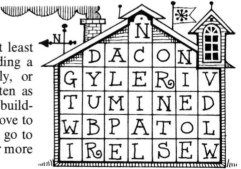

CAN YOU RHYME THESE CELEBRITIES?

Each of the lines of the two-line verses contains a clue for the name of a celebrity. The name should conclude the line in such a way as to produce a rhyme with the second name of each verse. Example: 1a) and 1b) EDISON—MADISON. Par score is 10 or more pairs of rhyming celebrities.

1a) Twelve hundred patents are ascribed to _____ .
1b) The Constitution was drawn up by _____ .

2a) *The Prince* was written by the schemer _____ .
2b) The painting "Birth of Venus" is by _____ .

3a) An Unconditional Surrender was asked for by _____ .
3b) *The Critique of Pure Reason* is a work by _____ .

4a) St. Paul's Cathedral was designed by _____ .
4b) The Quaker State was founded by a man named _____ .

5a) Washington's friend, a French Marquis, was _____ .
5b) A missionary and explorer was _____ .

6a) Medicine's father was _____ .
6b) A teaching philosopher was _____ .

7a) An author of great short stories was _____ .
7b) Britain's most famed cartoonist was _____ .

8a) Famous Italian, author, goldsmith was _____ .
8b) *Norma* is the best known opera by _____ .

9a) The *Songs of Innocence* is by the poet-artist _____ .
9b) The Armada was defeated by the seaman _____ .

10a) The text of the "Star-Spangled Banner" is by _____ .
10b) The South's most famous general was _____ .

11a) The oratorio *The Messiah* is by _____ .
11b) The laws of heredity were found by _____ .

12a) The telephone inventor was the Scotchman _____ .
12b) The hero of Swiss independence was _____ .

13a) A great Italian poet was Torquato _____ .
13b) The founder of cubism is Pablo _____ .

14a) The fingerprinting theory we owe to _____ .
14b) The Atomic theory goes back to _____ .

15a) One of the great stars of golf is _____ .
15b) The famous army doctor is called _____ .

16a) The author of *The American Dream* is _____ .
16b) A pretty actress is _____ .

17a) A man of common sense was called _____ .
17b) A humorous man was Mark _____ .
18a) A recent English philosopher was named _____ .
18b) A "darling" of stage and screen was _____ .
19a) Ike's Vice-President was named _____ .
19b) One of Santa's reindeer is _____ .
20a) A famous English politician was _____ .
20b) A famous race car driver is Phil _____ .

CAN YOU BEAT THE SONGWRITER?

This quiz may write *finis* to the efforts of most amateur songwriters in search of words that rhyme with JUNE or MOON. The 10 couplets below define the most important words that rhyme with either JUNE or MOON, each line being a definition for one such word. The answer to the first couplet is, of course, MOON and JUNE. Get 7 or more of the others and Tin Pan Alley may have a place for you.

1a) To wander, to idle and to stare aside;
1b) The month devoted to the bride.

2a) To puff out, distend, or inflate;
2b) An ancient Roman magistrate.

3a) To call in question, contradict;
3b) A wrecker, pirate, derelict.

4a) Convenient not, nor reasonable;
4b) An ape, short-tailed, unreasonable.

5a) Exempt from tax, from sieges free;
5b) At night, it likes to climb a tree.

6a) A blessing, favor, gift of plenty;
6b) In substance wanting, also scanty.

7a) To urge persistently, to tease;
7b) A hurricane of China's seas.

8a) To trim, lop off, and cut to size;
8b) A craven coward you despise.

9a) Bring into harmony, accord;
9b) A financial magnate like, for instance, Ford.

10a) To put ashore and leave alone;
10b) The god who rules the ocean zones.

CAN YOU PASS THE BUCK LOGICALLY?

Can you arrange the eight scenes shown here in their correct logical order, so that the passing of the buck makes one full turn, so to speak?

HOW QUICK-WITTED ARE YOU?

1. EXPERT EXPLANATION

What would you tell an expert who tells you that, probably as the result of easier accessibility of poisons, the proportion of undetected murders has risen from 15.7% to 26.6% in the last ten years.

2. DIVISION IS VEXATION

Can you make this row of figures divisible by 9 without leaving a remainder, altering a figure, adding a new one, or taking one away?

6 9 0 6 1 0 8 9 1 9 8

3. ARE YOU SISTER-AND-BROTHERWISE?

A boy said: "I have as many brothers as sisters." His sister, however, maintained that she had twice as many brothers as sisters. Can you tell how many brothers and sisters there were in all?

4. UNTIMELY HOMECOMING

A husband coming home in the wee hours of the morning wondered what time it was, but a glance at his watch told him nothing; it had stopped at 12:30. Without consulting any other timepiece, radio, stars, or person, he tiptoed to bed. Yet the next day when his good wife asked him when he had come home he could reply truthfully: "At two thirty." How could he know?

SLEIGHT OF MIND

FOUR CARDS HERE: Under an ace there is an ace. Over a heart there is a spade. Under an ace, there is a king, and under a diamond there is a heart. A heart is over a diamond, and an ace is under a king. Which cards have been dealt?

SHELL GAME VARIETY

If you know that a diamond lies to the left of a spade, that a two lies to the right of a jack, and a nine to the left of a club, and a club to the left of a spade, can you then tell which cards are hiding their faces.

CHIEF OR THIEF?

Here are a number of words for people who, in some way, either lead or steal. Can you determine who is a CHIEF and who is a THIEF?

1. Picaroon	8. Privateer
2. Coryphée	9. Nizam
3. Fugleman	10. Sirdar
4. Sachem	11. Buccaneer
5. Peculator	12. Dacoit
6. Tycoon	13. Plagiarist
7. Sagamore	14. Mosstrooper

HOW'S YOUR GUESSWORK?

You are NOT asked here to supply a correct solution to the following problems, though each of them does have an answer that may be arrived at in various ways. Just try to make as good a GUESS as possible. We suggest that you gather your family and friends around to determine who is the best guesser.

1. A murder was discovered at 9 o'clock Monday morning. The person who discovered it told three people about it between 9 and 9:15. Let us assume that each of these people told the news of the murder to three other people in the quarter hour from 9:15 to 9:30 and that in each ensuing hour all the people who had just heard the news told it to three other people who did not already know about it. If it were possible that the news about the murder could thus be communicated to all people living on earth (about 3 billion), by what time—would you GUESS—will the news have reached all people living at present?

2. What odds—would you GUESS—are in a bet that there are at least two people on earth who have exactly the same number of hairs on their head?

3. On what date—would you GUESS—had or will have elapsed a period of 1,000,000,000 minutes from the beginning of the Christian era?

4. How many different colors—would you GUESS—does a mapmaker need in order to avoid the possibility of painting countries that border each other the same color?

5. Suppose you have 15 books and you are one of those people who like to re-arrange things. How long—would you GUESS—would all possible re-arrangements of the 15 books take if each re-arrangement took up just 1 second of your time?

6. How much dust (in weight)—would you GUESS—does an inhabitant of a big city inhale during an average lifetime?

7.
```
                A
              M   M
            E   E   E
          R   R   R   R
        I   I   I   I   I
      C   C   C   C   C   C
    A   A   A   A   A   A   A
```

How often—would you GUESS—can the word AMERICA be spelled by starting from the top of this pyramid of letters, always passing from one letter to the adjoining one?

8. Cork is a very light material, as everyone knows. A bottle cork weighs "almost nothing." How heavy—would you GUESS—will be a 4-yard-high sphere made entirely of cork?

9. A panhandler asked a nabob for a gift. The nabob was in a good mood and gave him $20. This looked promising. The panhandler went again to see the nabob, who then gave him $10. This was not bad either, and the man tried his luck again on the next day when he got $5. From then on, he visited the nabob every day. How much money—would you GUESS—will the panhandler have accumulated following this procedure for an entire year, always receiving half the amount he received on the preceding day?

10. Suppose that a man, from the moment of his birth, would pay $1 for each beat of his heart. What age—would you GUESS—would this man have to attain to be able to pay for the entire cost for the atomic bomb research prior to exploding the first bomb ($2 billion)?

RIDDLES, RIDDLES, RIDDLES

1. Why did the man rob the glue factory?
2. What is the best way to make a fire with two sticks?
3. What did the bald man say when he got a comb on his birthday?
4. There are six of us in every family, but only four in a town; what are we?
5. What's the difference between a ghost and a walking weak sailor?
6. What inventions have helped men up in the world?
7. What, by losing an eye, has nothing left but a nose?
8. How do you know that flowers are lazy?
9. I have cities but no houses; forests but no trees; rivers without water. What am I?
10. Why is a bad riddle like a poor pencil?
11. What would you have if a bird got caught in your lawn mower?
12. What wheel goes around without touching the ground?
13. Why is a railroad engine like the family wash?
14. What 10-letter word starts with g-a-s?
15. How can you stand two inches away from another person without his being able to touch you?
16. What is the only nail a carpenter hates to hit?

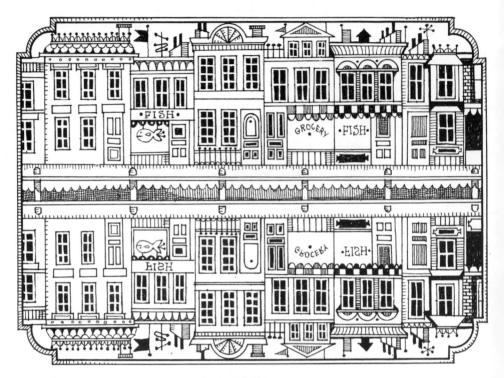

HOW 'MIRROR'ABLE ARE YOU?

I. Study the illustration of the houses on the waterfront carefully and see how many mistakes you can find in the mirror image.

II. Don Quixote has given up fighting windmills to challenge mirrors. Your task is to find eight instances in which the picture of our heroic Knight at the right differs from the picture at the left.

WHAT GOES ON IN THE LETTER CIRCLE?

For an explanation of how best to solve this puzzle, please turn to page 17.

FOR YOUNGSTERS

A) A long deep wound
B) American industrialist
C) Insect
D) Rain
E) The fiftieth
F) Jerome _____: Composer
G) Ship's place
H) Steal
I) British playwright
J) Sea eagle
K) Fuel
L) Sewing machine inventor
M) Performance
N) Tree or its berry
O) Tough wood
P) _____ Bruce: King
Q) In what way
R) Debtor
S) Sprite
T) Catch
U) Pro
V) Garment
W) Give assent
X) Nucleus
Y) St. _____ of Loyola
Z) Our country

FOR PARENTS

A) Crook's alternative
B) Saint
C) Tree
D) Another tree
E) State
F) Colonel's homonym
G) Ballet painter
H) Bird
I) Model T man
J) Bride's party
K) Fly
L) Elias
M) Cut
N) Puritan clergyman
O) Billet
P) Unsocial Socialist
Q) Roy
R) _____to-do
S) Bruce
T) "Oh, Boy" boy
U) Have debts
V) Mantle
W) _____ business
X) _____ all the world
Y) Light or dark
Z) Ourselves twice

101

FAMILY QUIZ GAME

For an introduction to this popular *Parents' Magazine* FAMILY QUIZ GAME please turn to page 18.

FOR MOTHERS
POETRY

(1) Who wrote the poem "The Hollow Men"? (2) A pair of lines whose end words rhyme is a _____ . (3) What famous American poet was born in Amherst, Mass., and lived there almost all her life? (4) Complete the name of this famous poet: Algernon Charles _____ . (5) True or false: Johann Wolfgang von Goethe, German poet, was a leading figure in the Romantic movement. (6) Who said: " 'Tis better to have loved and lost, than never to have loved at all"? (7) Who wrote: "The Night Before Christmas"? (8) Another name for a symphonic poem is _____ . (9) What famous English poet, buried in Rome, has these words on his tombstone: "Here lies one whose name was writ in water"? (10) What famous American poet died in 1967?

FOR FATHERS:
GOVERNMENT

(1) Senator _____ is Chairman of the Senate Foreign Relations Committee. (2) How can the Senate expel a member? (3) Who presides over the U.S. Senate? (4) What body can reject a Presidential appointee to the Supreme Court? (5) At least how many Supreme Court Justices must agree so that a decision may be handed down? (6) During whose administration was the constitutional amendment passed that limited the Presidency to two terms? (7) What really makes a bill law? (8) By whom is a Congressman-at-large elected? (9) In the House and Senate chambers, which is the certain symbol of authority? (10) When do the electors meet to cast their vote for President?

FOR YOUNGSTERS (5¾—6 YEARS)

GEOGRAPHY

(1) What European country is shaped like a boot? (2) The Golden Gate bridge is located in what state? (3) Where is the capital of the U.S. located? (4) True or false: New Mexico is a country. (5) Which is larger, a country or a continent? (6) If you were going to Alaska, would you take light or heavy clothing? (7) The area between two mountains is called a a. desert b. valley c. hill. (8) Which is the biggest, a. stream b. river c. brook? (9) Name the U.S. state in which Eskimos live. (10) The opposite of East is _____ .

FOR JUNIORS (6½-9 YEARS)

PLANES & FIGURES

(1) What is a shorter way of saying five thousand thousand? (2) How many angles are there in a triangle? (3) Does a trapezoid have two or four parallel sides? (4) How many inches in three feet? (5) There are _____ notes in an octave. (6) In counting by tens what number follows ninety? (7) How many five-cent stamps in a dozen? (8) If you divide a square with a diagonal, what shapes will you have? (9) Write 33 in Roman numerals (10) How many sides has a cube?

FOR PRE-TEENS (10–12 YEARS)

NATURAL HISTORY

(1) We get silk from the _____ of a silkworm. (2) Which tree keeps its leaves all winter? (3) What animal will not eat food it has not washed? (4) Where are natural sponges found? (5) A gnu is most like a a. buffalo b. antelope c. goat (6) Does the date fruit come from a tree or is it found by digging into the ground? (7) True or false: The porpoise is a mammal. (8) Do insects have lungs? (9) An alligator pear is also called an _____ . (10) Which bird migrates from one pole to the other?

FOR YOUNG TEENS (13–15 YEARS)

FIRST AND LAST

(1) Who made the first American flag? (2) The first state to enter the Union was _____ . (3) The last state to enter the Union was _____ . (4) The first state to ratify the Constitution was _____ . (5) The state capital with the greatest population is _____ . (6) Arrange in size from smallest to largest: Earth, Moon, Sun. (7) Which city of the world ranks first in population. (8) The first book of the Old Testament is called _____ . (9) What is the first word of the "Gettysburg Address." (10) The name of the first U.S. satellite to go into orbit was _____ .

THE MOST RIDICULOUS GAME EVER PLAYED

The picture above gives a snapshot of a soccer game during the first half of the game; the one below depicts the situation after half-time.

Compare both illustrations and try to find 8 patent absurdities.

AUGUST

CALENDAR OF MEMORABLE DATES

1 World War I began, 1914	**2** Pierre L'Enfant, 1754–1825, designer of Washington, D.C.	**3** Christopher Columbus set sail from Palos, Spain, 1492	**4**
5 Guy de Maupassant, 1850–93, famous French short-story writer	**6** Atomic bomb dropped on Hiroshima	**7** Canada-U. S. Peace Bridge dedicated, 1927	**8**
9	**10** Smithsonian Institute founded, 1846 Herbert Hoover, 1874–1964, 31st U. S. President	**11** Fulton's steamship, "Clermont," 1807	**12** Julius Rosenwald, 1862–1932, American philanthropist Katherine Bates, 1859–1929. Wrote "America the Beautiful"
13 William Caxton, 1422–91, first English printer and type designer	**14** Atlantic Charter— formulated by Churchill and Roosevelt —announced 1941	**15** Panama Canal opened to shipping, 1914	**16** Gold discovered in Klondike, 1896
17 David Crockett, 1786–1836, frontiersman and Indian Scout	**18** M. Lewis, 1774–1809, leader of the Lewis and Clark Expedition to the northwest, 1804–05	**19** Orville Wright, 1871–1948, American inventor. Flew first airplane with brother Wilbur, at Kitty Hawk, 1903	**20** Benjamin Harrison, 1833–1901, 23rd President
21 Lincoln-Douglas debates began, 1858	**22** Claude Debussy, 1862–1918, French composer	**23** Oliver Perry, 1785–1819, famed American naval hero, won battle of Lake Erie, 1813	**24** British burned Washington, D.C., 1814
25 Pompeii destroyed by eruption of Mt. Vesuvius, A.D. 79	**26** 19th amendment giving vote to women, put into effect, 1920	**27** First oil well drilled in Pennsylvania, 1859	**28** Johann von Goethe, 1749–1832, German poet
29 John Locke, 1632–1704, English philosopher Oliver Wendell Holmes, 1809–94, American poet	**30**	**31** Charleston, S.C., earthquake, 1886. Most disastrous quake east of Mississippi	

VOYAGES TO NOWHERE

In this travel month of August when each and everybody is going in each and every direction, we are taking an excursion into NOWHERE. Can you identify from the clues given below the names of the places that do not actually exist but have been created either by traditional beliefs or highly imaginative writers? With a score of 9 or more correct you will get NOWHERE fast.

WHAT LEGENDARY PLACE . . .

1. _____ mentioned by Homer, Plato and Horace, was later described by Lord Bacon in a piece of allegoric fiction as representing a model arrangement for the promotion of science and the perfection of man as a social being.
2. _____ is said to have been discovered by John Scalvë, and is supposed to represent a vast tract of land near the Arctic Circle in North America.
3. _____ was created by Thomas More as a perfect example for a place where everything is flawless: the law, the morals, even the politics.
4. _____ literally means delight and pleasure and is regarded as the site of the origin of the human race.
5. _____ is full of idleness and luxury, "where the houses are made of barley sugar and cakes, the streets are paved with pastry, and the shops supply goods without requiring money in payment."
6. _____ in satirical fiction is inhabited by a race of pygmies to whom an ordinary human being appeared as a monstrous giant.
7. _____ is full of "gigantic giants" to whom the same ordinary human being appeared as "a pygmy not half so big as a round little worm plucked from the lazy finger of a maid."
8. _____ was one of the destinations of Hercules, from where he was supposed to bring back the Golden Apples which Hera had received as a marriage gift—the place which was guarded by certain sisters with the help of a dragon.
9. _____ was believed by Orellana, one of Pizarro's lieutenants, to be a land of gold and unbounded wealth between the Amazon and Orinoco Rivers.
10. _____ in Nordic mythology was inhabited by the immortal souls of heroes slain in battle.
11. _____ "is formed of divine light beyond the power of description; each inhabitant of which was bigger than the whole earth and had 70,000 heads, each of which had 70,000 mouths with each mouth having 70,000 tongues and each tongue speaking 70,000 languages."
12. _____ was depicted by the Greek poets as the fair land where the souls of the good dwelled and to which the great heroes passed without death and in the ideal climate of which they were always happy.

COMPETITIVE WORD GAMES FOR ALL

THE SHORT WORD WINS!

Find the *shortest possible* word by adding as FEW letters as possible to *each* side of each letter pair. (No S-endings or proper nouns!) Example: 4. sPIt. Score 1 point for each letter added, 10 points if you are unable to make up a word. In some instances you will be able to find a word shorter than the answer provided. PAR SCORE is 36 points.

1. _____H Y_____   7. _____O H_____
2. _____A A_____   8. _____L Y_____
3. _____P D_____   9. _____I P_____
4. _____P I_____   10. _____D P_____
5. _____Y L_____   11. _____A A_____
6. _____H O_____   12. _____Y H_____

THE LONG WORD WINS!

Find the *longest possible* word that can be spelled from the letters in each of the words below. Score as many points for each word as it has letters. Example: 1. Get the word MOANS from the word HANSOM and score 5 points for it. In some instances you will be able to make a word longer than the answer provided. PAR SCORE is 84 points.

1. _____ HANSOM   7. _____ OBSTETRIC
2. _____ ARDENT   8. _____ LIBERATOR
3. _____ PIONEER   9. _____ INDICATIVE
4. _____ PELICAN   10. _____ DENOUEMENT
5. _____ YULETIDE   11. _____ ALTERATIONS
6. _____ HISTORIC   12. _____ YESTERNIGHT

EYE SPY

Two of the faces are alike in all respects. Are you enough of a spy to eye which two?

....the text of an opera

CAN YOU GET THE WRITERS RIGHT?

The main occupation of the people in the left column is writing. How and in what kind of writing each of them is specializing is set forth in detail in the right column in mixed order. Can you match both columns and thus tell a scribe from a scribbler? A score of 10 or more is very good.

WHICH OF THESE PEOPLE . . . SPECIALIZES IN WRITING . . .

1. Allegorist
2. Amanuensis
3. Anecdotist
4. Annalist

5. Calligrapher
6. Fabulist
7. Ghost
8. Hack

9. Legman
10. Librettist

11. Novelist
12. Pamphleteer

13. Registrar
14. Scenarist
15. Transcriber

a) fiction prose portraying real life characters in a plot.
b) the text of an opera.
c) as a decorative art by having an especially elegant handwriting.
d) records containing regular entries of items or details.
e) brief, usually controversial treatises.
f) historic events in chronological order.
g) the plot of a movie.
h) a brief account of some real or fictitious incident.
i) from dictation or copying manuscript.
j) arrangements of a composition for an instrument different from the one for which it was written.
k) informative items of spot news.
l) any sort of literary work he has hired himself out for.
m) what somebody else publishes as his own.
n) highly fictitious stories embodying a moral.
o) symbolic representations illustrating a truth.

The ripest fruit first......

TO QUOTE OR TO MISQUOTE...

The following quotations are often used in everyday speech. Can you tell which version is the correct one? Your QUOTABILITY is unquestioned if you get 15 or more correctly.

1. A little (knowledge) (learning) is a dangerous thing.
2. A word to the wise is (enough) (sufficient).
3. Fresh (fields) (woods) and pastures new.
4. Food for (cannons) (powder).
5. An empty barrel makes the (most) (loudest) noise.
6. To kill a wife with (love) (kindness).
7. The proof of the pudding (lies) (is) in the eating.
8. Truth is the truth to the end of (reckoning) (time).
9. Discretion is the (best) (better) part of valor.
10. As (happy) (merry) as the day is long.
11. Talkers are (never) (no) good doers.
12. The ripest fruit first (fall) (falls).
13. Sorrow treads upon the heels of (mirth) (glee).
14. Water, water everywhere, (nor any) (and not) a drop to drink.
15. All that (glisters) (glitters) is not gold.
16. When Greek (meets) (joins) Greek then comes the tug of war.
17. We are such stuff as dreams are made (of) (on).
18. The better foot (foremost) (before).
19. My love's (more richer) (richer) than my tongue.
20. I smell the blood of an (Englishman) (British man).

DREAM SHOP OF THE FUTURE—300 YEARS AGO

The store opened its doors in the 1660s. Maybe the genial owner mesmerized his customers into seeing some of the items that simply couldn't be there, or could they? Well, it is your task to decide. Spot most (if not all) of the items that it would have been impossible to even look at (let alone buy) in the 1660s. If you don't overlook more than 3 of these items, you are doing very well.

TREES IN THE LETTER FOREST

Concealed in the letter maze are at least 16 well-known trees. Move horizontally, vertically, or diagonally, and repeat letters as often as necessary to spell out the name of a tree. Example: Start with the upper H, go to O, double the L, and then go to Y and get HOLLY. A score of 11 and over is very good.

RIDDLES, RIDDLES, RIDDLES

1. Why is your heart like a policeman?
2. What is the least dangerous kind of robbery?
3. Why do gardeners hate weeds?
4. What is long and hard, has no feet, but wears shoes?
5. What is most useful when it is used up?
6. What binds two people together yet only touches one?
7. Why do people laugh up their sleeves?
8. If an egg came floating down the Hudson River, where would it come from?
9. What is the longest word in the English language?
10. Why is an icy sidewalk like music?
11. What is a forum?
12. What did the tree say to the axe?
13. What fruit kept best in Noah's ark?
14. What has no end and no beginning?
15. What ring is best for a telephone?
16. How do you know a baker is unselfish?
17. What animals have their eyes nearest together?
18. What is it that has four legs and a tail, eats oats, and sees equally well from both ends?
19. What is the last word in airplanes?
20. What does an envelope say when you lick it?
21. What goes up into the air white and comes down yellow and white?
22. What is it whose work is only to play?

THE GREAT MEMORY QUIZ

Study the illustration on page 112 for as long as you wish. When you think you can remember it sufficiently, cover the page with a piece of paper, then try to answer the questions on this page. Score 1 point for each question answered correctly by remembering the object seen and deduct 1 point for each wrong answer. A score of 30 is very, very good.

WOULD THE THINGS YOU SAW IN THE PICTURE ON PAGE 112 ENABLE YOU TO . . .

1. Drink a soda?
2. Take a bath?
3. Play a record?
4. Save some money?
5. Change a tire?
6. Pencil a note?
7. Sign a note?
8. Eat a potato?
9. Make a telephone call?
10. Draw a circle?
11. Paint a picture?
12. Snap a picture?
13. Keep your foot covered?
14. Keep your hand covered?
15. Bore a screw hole?
16. Put a screw in?
17. Protect yourself against rain?
18. Play chess?
19. Light a room?
20. Pay carfare?
21. Comb your dog?
22. Tell the time?
23. Tie up your boat?
24. Grind coffee?
25. Drink wine?
26. Remove a bottle cork?
27. Make an injection?
28. Type a letter?
29. Read better?
30. See better at a show?
31. Drive a nail into the wall?
32. Peel an apple?
33. Stamp a letter?
34. Jump from a plane?
35. Play cards?
36. Make fried eggs?
37. Draw a right angle?
38. Perfume a room?
39. Dig a ditch?
40. Drink tea?

FAMILY QUIZ GAME

For an introduction to this popular *Parents' Magazine* FAMILY QUIZ GAME please turn to page 18.

For an introduction to this popular *Parents' Magazine* FAMILY QUIZ GAME please turn to page 18.

FOR MOTHERS

MUSIC

(1) What is a hemidemisemiquaver? (2) What are the last names of these three great violinists: a. Fritz b. Yehudi c. Jascha? (3) Which type of music is often called "schmalz": a. modern b. jazz c. sweet? (4) Who founded the impressionist school in music? (5) Name the four classes of instruments in an orchestra. (6) From what was the name piano derived? (7) What American composer was known for his marches? (8) A musical composition in which one or a few instruments stand out against the rest of the orchestra is called a _____. (9) Who wrote the music and lyrics for "Guys and Dolls"? (10) A section of a musical composition which is formally distinct from the main structure, but is added as a conclusion is called a _____.

FOR FATHERS

U.S. HISTORY

(1) What unsuccessful presidential candidate said: "Sir, I would rather be right than President"? (2) During whose administration was the Louisiana Purchase made? (3) Who was the first leader of the Democratic Party? (4) What were the first two political parties in the U.S.? (5) The first national labor union was established in _____. (6) What amendment to the U.S. Constitution abolished slavery? (7) Who purchased Manhattan Island from the Indians? (8) What man has run for President of the U.S. six times? (9) Who was the first American President to go to Europe during his term of office? (10) Name the three Presidents before Lyndon Johnson who were also born West of the Mississippi.

FOR YOUNGSTERS (5–6 YEARS)

THE BODY

(1) The decayed spot in a tooth is called a _____. (2) How many thumbs do you have? (3) How many elbows? (4) True or false: You get your first permanent teeth when you are about six. (5) Add your fingers, your toes and your nose. (6) What is the smallest finger on your hand sometimes called? (7) The part of your body between your head and the shoulders is called the _____. (8) What do you use to smell with? (9) Which are longer, your arms or your legs? (10) The inside of your hand is called a _____ which is also a word for a tree.

FOR JUNIORS (6½–9 YEARS)

SHIPS

(1) Did the famous warship "Old Ironsides" really have iron sides? (2) What is a hawser? (3) What boat helps ocean liners come into dock? (4) What is the name of the ship that brought the first Pilgrims to New England? (5) The power that sailed a schooner came from a. steam b. gasoline c. wind. (6) What kind of boat can travel under the surface of the ocean? (7) Who in the Bible is said to have built an ark just before the flood? (8) True or false: A ship's prison is called a brig. (9) In what type of boat would you find a jib? (10) What naval officer said: "Damn the torpedoes, full steam ahead"?

FOR PRE-TEENS (10–12 YEARS)

AUTHORS

(1) Name the Danish author of fairy tales such as *The Red Shoes.* (2) Tom Sawyer and Huckleberry Finn were written by whom? (3) Who wrote the song "My Old Kentucky Home"? (4) In whose honor did Walt Whitman write the poem "O Captain, My Captain"? (5) True or false: The author of Robin Hood is unknown. (6) Who wrote the Tarzan books? (7) "In His Own Write" was written by _____. (8) What was the name of Benjamin Franklin's book of sayings? (9) Who wrote the novel *The Deerslayer*? (10) Who wrote most of the Declaration of Independence?

FOR YOUNG TEENS (13–15 YEARS)

MORE OR LESS

(1) Are there more books in the Old or in the New Testament? (2) Which is heaviest: One pound of feathers or one pound of steel? (3) Which is larger—a three foot square or three square feet? (4) Which gas is lighter —helium or hydrogen? (5) Which canal is longer—the Panama or the Suez? (6) An angle that is less than 90 degrees is often called an _____. (7) Which is worth more, the American dollar or the British pound? (8) True or false: There are more sheep in Australia than in any other country. (9) To make a bicycle pedal more easily, would we make the rear sprocket larger or smaller? (10) One liter is (more) (less) than one liquid quart?

WHAT GOES ON IN THE LETTER CIRCLE?

For an explanation of how to solve this puzzle best, please turn to page 17.

FOR YOUNGSTERS

A) Offspring
B) Hot place
C) Poet laureate
D) Skill
E) _____ Whitman
F) Tree
G) Battle of _____ Bay
H) Unruly crowd
 I) Sage
J) Map
K) _____ and Clark
L) "Show Me" State: Abbreviation
M) Burn
N) Bret _____: Author
O) Singing voice
P) Bombard
Q) "Remember the _____"
R) Large weight
S) Ocean
T) See
U) Percy Bysshe
V) Volunteer State: Abbreviation
W) Cotton State: Abbreviation
X) Ill humor
Y) Badger State: Abbreviation
Z) _____ de France

FOR PARENTS

A) Inferno
B) "Skylark" poet
C) Of sound
D) "Father of Angling"
E) Choler
F) Lord Alfred
G) All
H) Shoe size
 I) Where Crockett died
J) Explorer
K) Measure
L) _____ guy
M) City on Elbe
N) Masses
O) _____ Bay
P) Waters
Q) Cunning
R) Bret
S) Getaway
T) Alas
U) Sash
V) Evergreen
W) She in French
X) Illinois city
Y) French fashion
Z) Stag

SEPTEMBER

CALENDAR OF MEMORABLE DATES

1 World War II began, 1939, when Nazi Germany attacked Poland	**2** V-J Day, 1945	**3** Great Britain and France declared war on Germany, 1939	**4** Hudson discovered Manhattan Island, 1609
5	**6** Mayflower sailed from England, 1620	**7**	**8**
9 California became the 31st state, 1850	**10**	**11**	**12**
13 British defeated the French in the Battle of Quebec, 1759—turning point of the French and Indian War	**14** Birthday of "The Star Spangled Banner," 1814	**15** William Howard Taft, 1857–1930, 27th President, 1909–13; Chief Justice of Supreme Court, 1921–30	**16**
17	**18** Washington laid the Capitol building cornerstone, 1793	**19** Mickey Mouse made movie debut, 1928	**20** Alexander the Great, 356–323 B.C.—world conqueror; patron of the arts and sciences
21	**22** First day of autumn	**23** American Indian Day	**24** John Marshall, 1755–1835—fourth Chief Justice
25 Balboa discovered the Pacific Ocean, 1513	**26** Night and day equal length	**27** Women first admitted to Democratic National Committee, 1919	**28**
29 Michaelmas Day—the feast of the Archangels Michael, Gabriel and Raphael	**30**		

HOW SOUNDWISE ARE YOU?

Back to school this month, and with it comes a combination spelling and pronunciation test that may be a challenge to any grade. For each of the words in the various categories below there are one or more other words that are pronounced exactly alike but spelled differently. The answer to 1, for example, is BARE.

You are a sound wizard if you as a youngster get 12 or more of your group right and if you as a parent get 45 or more of the sound-alikes in your groups correctly.

FOR YOUNGSTERS

1. bear ____	6. hare ____	11. lie ___
2. steak _____	7. peak ____	12. feat ____
3. son ___	8. die ___	13. main ____
4. tens _____	9. too ___	14. fare ____
5. leek ____	10. pair ____	15. sore ____

FOR PARENTS

EASY	NOT SO EASY	NOT AT ALL EASY
1. miner _____	13. marshall _____	25. sucker _____
2. horse _____	14. air ____	26. climb _____
3. alter _____	15. cannon _____	27. kernel _____
4. plum _____	16. cast _____	28. fate ____
5. pain ____	17. auger _____	29. choir _____
6. night _____	18. bow ____	30. palate _____
7. high ___	19. root _____	31. deviser _____
8. horde _____	20. plate _____	32. crews _____
9. fourth _____	21. earn ___	33. reek _____
10. raise ____	22. doe _____	34. sign ____
11. eye ___	23. rime _____	35. barren _____
12. faint _____	24. done ___	36. rough ____

DIFFICULT

37. rain	a)____	b)_____	42. meet	a)____	b)____
38. new	a)___	b)____	43. site	a)_____	b)____
39. bell	a)___	b)_____	44. vain	a)____	b)____
40. write	a)_____	b)_____	45. idle	a)____	b)____
41. frees	a)_____	b)_____	46. you	a)___	b)___

COMPETITIVE WORD GAMES FOR ALL

THE SHORT WORD WINS!

Find the *shortest possible* word by adding as FEW letters as possible to *each* side of each letter pair. (No S-endings or proper nouns!) Example: 2. mANe. Score 1 point for each letter added, 10 points if you are unable to make up a word. In some instances you will be able to find a word shorter than the answer provided. PAR SCORE is 31 points.

1. ____H	S____	7. ____T	S____
2. ____A	N____	8. ____M	E____
3. ____R	O____	9. ____O	V____
4. ____V	O____	10. ____O	R____
5. ____E	M____	11. ____N	A____
6. ____S	T____	12. ____S	H____

THE LONG WORD WINS!

Find the *longest possible* word that can be spelled from the letters in each of the words below. Score as many points for each word as it has letters. Example: 1. Get the word HURLED from the word HURDLE and score 6 points for it. In some instances you will be able to make a word longer than the answer provided. PAR SCORE is 86 points.

1. _____HURDLE	7. _____THIRTIETH
2. _____AIRMEN	8. _____MARMOSETS
3. _____RECLAIM	9. _____ORTHOPEDIC
4. _____VERDICT	10. _____OBLIGATION
5. _____ETHEREAL	11. _____NIGHTINGALE
6. _____SOBRIETY	12. _____STRANGULATE

A GRAVE ERROR

Something is wrong with the inscription on this tombstone. Can you guess what it is?

·IN·MEMORY·
·OF·
JOHN·SMITH
DIED FEB 3,1864
·AGE 89 YRS·
·AND·
MOLLY·SMITH
·HIS·WIDOW·
DIED NOV 4,1858
·AGE 84 YRS·

GEOGRAPHY: TRUE, FALSE, OR BOTH?

The statements below refer to 3 possible meanings of one geographical word. Of these, one may be correct, two may be correct, or all three may be correct. On the other hand, there may be instances when all three meanings are incorrect. It's up to you to decide. Score 20 points for each correct answer. A score of 20 or more correctly identified word meanings is very good.

1. JERSEY, a channel island
   a) a fine woolen yarn
   b) a State of the Union
   c) a breed of cattle
2. TROY, ruined city in Asia
   a) a city in New York
   b) a system of weight
   c) a very heavy cigar
3. BERLIN, old German capital
   a) a worsted yarn
   b) a four-wheeled carriage
   c) a canoe
4. PANAMA, in Central America
   a) a fine straw hat
   b) a very long cigarette
   c) a sweetened bread dish
5. WINCHESTER, an English city
   a) a sharp pungent sauce
   b) a sporting firearm
   c) a traveling bag
6. PEKING, capital of China
   a) a kind of green tea
   b) a large duck
   c) a striped satin fabric

7. ARRAS, a French city
   a) a kind of police dog
   b) a wall tapestry
   c) an ardent spirit
8. ASTRAKHAN, a Russian city
   a) a carpet of long pile
   b) a long-haired dog
   c) a long curled fur
9. TOLEDO, a Spanish city
   a) a fine-tempered sword
   b) a pink rose
   c) a reversible linen fabric
10. GENEVA, a Swiss city
    a) a black academic gown
    b) a Alpine variety of Gentian
    c) a kind of gin
11. MADRAS, an Indian city
    a) a large bright kerchief
    b) a sweet wine
    c) a rattan cane
12. JAPAN, an Asiatic country
    a) a quince-like shrub
    b) a natural varnish
    c) a small leaf chafer

120

'STATE'LY EXPRESSIONS

Some of our states have produced certain specialties whose names do not tell the uninitiated immediately what they stand for. Match 11 or more of the 'state'ly expressions in the left column with their correct meanings in the right column, and be 'state'wide victor.

1. Georgia belle
2. Texas tommy
3. Alabama slider
4. Florida earth
5. Arkansas black
6. Kentucky mahogany
7. Rhode Island Red
8. Arizona ruby
9. New York point
10. Carolina allspice
11. Virginia reel
12. Iowa crab
13. Ohio round
14. Oregon box
15. Mississippi bubble

a) The strawberry shrub
b) A wild, sour apple
c) A low, evergreen shrub
d) A country dance for many participants
e) A certain number of shots in archery
f) A white-fleshed peach
g) A freshwater tortoise
h) A filter medium in fat and oil refinery
i) A ragtime dance similar to the bunnyhug
j) A brittle, transparent silicate
k) A coffee tree
l) A speculative scheme for colonization
m) An important breed of fowl
n) A modification of Braille
o) A winter apple

COSMOPOLITAN COOKING

This menu may not be exactly what a gourmet would advise and, though it sounds interesting enough, we don't suggest you try to eat your way through it. What we do suggest is that you tag each of the dishes with its parent country. Thirteen plates correct and you could order a dinner anywhere.

1. Caviar
2. Bouillabaisse
3. Chicken Gumbo
4. Ravioli
5. Goulash
6. Hasenpfeffer
7. Tamale
8. Curry
9. Beef Stroganoff
10. Plum Pudding
11. Apple Strudel
12. Sherbet
13. Sherry
14. Gruyère Cheese
15. Mocha
16. Pilsen

LET'S BE PRANKSTERS!

Nobody likes a jokester who delights in pranks that injure or embarrass someone or that damage property. On the other hand, most people are good enough sports to enjoy a harmless joke, especially if it's really funny.

FORTUNE-TELLING TEETH

"Did you know," asks the prankster, "that it is possible to tell a person's fortune by the tooth marks he makes when he bites something soft?"

To prove it, the prankster rolls up a table napkin or clean handkerchief, then asks the victim to put it between his teeth and bite hard. The prankster takes back the napkin, studies the tooth marks carefully.

"You certainly bit on that one!" he says with a smile.

AROUND THE CORNER

The prankster goes up to someone who is standing near the corner of a house or building. "Would you mind holding this end of the string for a moment?" he asks. He hands the victim one end of a piece of cord about twenty feet long. Then he proceeds to walk away slowly, around the corner of the house, pulling the cord taut as he goes.

The victim obligingly holds the string for a while, but after several minutes have gone by he gets impatient. If he looks around the corner, what does he see? The prankster has simply tied the other end of the string to something, then completely vanished from the scene!

THE HYPNOTIC PLATES

"Have you ever been hypnotized?" asks the prankster. "I can do it with these two dinner plates." He hands one plate to the victim. They face each other, holding the plates as shown.

"You must look me straight in the eye at all times," continues the prankster, "and do exactly what I do.

The prankster rubs the bottom of his plate with his fingers, then he rubs the tip of his nose. The victim of course does the same. The prankster rubs the plate again, then rubs his forehead. He repeats with his cheeks and chin.

The victim doesn't know that the prankster has previously blackened

122

the bottom of one plate by holding a burning candle under it. After the victim's face is well covered with soot, the prankster tells him to look at himself in a mirror!

THE HIDDEN PROFIT

The prankster borrows a half dollar from the victim. He places it on the table next to a dime of his own, then covers both coins with a book.

"Would you be willing to pay a quarter for whatever is under this book?" he asks.

"Certainly," replies the unsuspecting victim.

"Okay," says the prankster. "You give me a quarter and I'll give you whatever you find under the book. You can even take a peek first before you pay me."

You'll be surprised at how many innocent people will pay a quarter for the sixty cents before they realize that they are buying back their own half dollar. The prankster makes a clear profit of fifteen cents!

THE KIDDIE CAR RIDE

The prankster splits the bottom of a paper match, folding the two halves at right angles as shown below. He asks the seated victim to hold the match as shown in the picture, then shuffle his feet back and forth on the floor.

After the poor fellow has done this for a half-minute or so, the prankster pats him on the shoulder and says, "Well, how do you like your new kiddie car?"

THE MUMMIFIED FINGER

"Would you like to see a human finger?" the prankster asks. "I have an uncle who is a surgeon. He just sent me one."

The prankster holds out a small cardboard box. When the victim takes off the cover, he is horrified to see a real finger inside, resting on cotton! What the victim doesn't know is that the box has a hole in the bottom (see illustration) through which the prankster has put his own middle finger!

A TEMPESTUOUS PROBLEM

This road company was surprised by a strong gust, and gone with the wind were all the hats. Can you reunite the correct hat with its rightful owner? If you can, the letters spelled out in correct numerical order will reveal the pertinent part of a well known quotation, unmasking the culprit of our little drama.

COUNTRY IDYL SLIGHTLY WACKY

How many of the dozen mistakes committed by the artist of this peaceful country scene can you discover? Find ten or more and you have done well here.

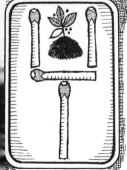

BE A MATCH-MAGICIAN

By moving only TWO matches, can you make a spade without the sand on it?

WHO MISSED THE ARK?

Almost everybody has embarked on the Ark, but if you look closely you'll see that some of the animals' counterparts are missing. Identify the ones that are only singly represented here and then take their last letters, and you will see that someone else, a VIP indeed, is also missing.

WHAT GOES ON IN THE LETTER CIRCLE?

For an explanation of how to solve this puzzle best, please turn to page 17.

FOR YOUNGSTERS

A) Cereal
B) President
C) Dog
D) Wild hog

E) *The Pathfinder* author
F) In what way
G) Propel
H) Still
I) Patriot Nathan
J) Wealthy
K) Two-masted ship
L) Ladle
M) Beer
N) Lake Erie victor
O) Greek letter
P) Equip
Q) Be indebted
R) Nordic name
S) Large snake
T) *Charge of the Light* _____
U) More healthy
V) Chicken house

W) Spider's work
X) Society girl
Y) Make mistakes
Z) Commercial

FOR PARENTS

A) Roam
B) William Howard
C) Girl
D) "We have met the enemy and they are ours" author
E) Bread
F) Patriot
G) Network
H) "The Light _____"
I) German I
J) Pacific discoverer
K) Beat
L) Vestment
M) Author
N) Hog
O) Washington conqueror
P) Alcoholic drink
Q) Non-alcoholic drink
R) Prison
S) Old coin
T) Plutocrat
U) Scarf
V) Alexander: Patron of the _____ and sciences
W) Latvian city
X) Victuals
Y) Italian W. W. II marshal
Z) Bill's companion

127

FAMILY QUIZ GAME

For an introduction to this popular *Parents' Magazine* FAMILY QUIZ GAME please turn to page 18.

FOR MOTHERS

FOOD

(1) What fruit do you associate with a. Bartlett b. Elberta c. Baldwin? (2) A connoisseur of food and drink is called an _____ . (3) Fish, eggs, lean meats are the chief source of a. minerals b. proteins c. fats. (4) What is the loganberry a cross between? (5) Sukiyaki is a popular meal in which country? (6) What vegetable does not belong in the following group: potatoes, onions, cabbage, carrots? (7) Who first developed the cultivation of corn? (8) Who said: "There is no spectacle more appealing than that of a beautiful woman in the act of cooking dinner for someone she loves"? (9) Gruyère is a kind of _____ . (10) A French fish chowder, seasoned and always made of two kinds of fish, is called a _____ .

FOR FATHERS

STAGE

(1) Who wrote *Incident at Vichy*? (2) What famous Greek play tells of a king who kills his father and marries his mother? (3) In which of Shakespeare's tragedies do these lines appear: "Double, double, toil and trouble. . . ."? (4) *Rigoletto* is an opera by what composer? (5) What actor is famous for his portrayal of Lincoln on the stage? (6) In what two operas do we find Figaro? (7) The original partner of composer Richard Rogers was _____ . (8) Most of Shakespeare's plays were first presented in the _____ Theater. (9) What late writer is considered America's most important dramatist? (10) Who was "The Great Profile".

FOR YOUNGSTERS (5–6 YEARS)

UNITED STATES

(1) Extremely tall buildings are called _____ . (2) When did Columbus discover America? (3) The President and his family live in a building called the _____ . (4) The city with the largest population is _____ . (5) Who first celebrated Thanksgiving? (6) Wampum is an Indian word for _____ . (7) Who was our first President? (8) An American Indian baby is called a _____ . (9) A presidential election is held every _____ years. (10) The person who would take over if the President could not fulfill the duties of his office is the _____ .

FOR JUNIORS (6½–9 YEARS)

STORYBOOK CHARACTERS

(1) Which bed was just right for Goldilocks, the big one, the middle sized one, or the small one? (2) What animal did Alice follow down the hole into Wonderland? (3) In what city did the Wizard of Oz live? (4) The little boy who is Winnie-the-Pooh's friend is _____ . (5) Name the pirate Captain in Peter Pan. (6) In *"The Jungle Book"* the little boy raised by animals is named _____ . (7) On what did the Sleeping Beauty prick her finger? (8) What is the real name of Agent 007? (9) What was the name of the tiny people in the book "Gulliver's Travels"? (10) Scrooge was noted for being a _____ .

FOR PRE-TEENS (10–12 YEARS)

SPACE

(1) American spaceships containing two astronauts are called _____ . (2) The moon completes an orbit around the earth in approximately a. 360 b. 1 c. 30 days. (3) How many visible stars are there in the Big Dipper? (4) What star is called the North Star? (5) How many planets are in our solar system? (6) The three dimensions of space are _____ , _____ , and _____ . (7) Give the true name of the planet often called the red planet. (8) Which planet has rings? (9) What star is closest to our planet earth? (10) The largest reflector telescope in the world is located where?

FOR YOUNG TEENS (13–15 YEARS)

DISCOVERERS

(1) Explorer Marco Polo traveled into China to the court of what ruler? (2) Did Polo live before or after Columbus? (3) What explorer searched for the Fountain of Youth? (4) Who discovered the Pacific Ocean? (5) What Spanish explorer discovered the Mississippi River? (6) Who discovered the X-ray? (7) What woman was the co-discoverer of radium? (8) Who discovered the North Pole? (9) the South Pole? (10) For the discovery of what country did Francisco Pizarro become famous?

ODD OBJECTS OUT! ! !

Each of the groups of 4 or 5 pictures has one object that does not logically belong in the group. Can you find it? A score of 14 or more ODD OBJECTS found is very good.

COLUMN A   COLUMN B   COLUMN C

OCTOBER

CALENDAR OF MEMORABLE DATES

1 James Lawrence, 1781–1813, said, "Don't give up the ship!"	**2** Mohandas Gandhi, 1869–1948	**3** Child Health Day "Jazz Singer," first talking picture, opened in NYC, 1927	**4** Rutherford B. Hayes, 1822–1893, 19th President (1877–81); Governor of Ohio
5 Chester Arthur, 1830–86, became President upon Garfield's death	**6**	**7**	**8**
9 Chicago fire, 1871	**10** Giusseppi Verdi, 1813–1901, great Italian opera composer U.S. Naval Academy opened in 1845	**11** Pulaski Day—honors Polish Count who died in American Revolution	**12** Columbus Day
13	**14** Battle of Hastings, 1066	**15** Gregorian calendar first introduced in 1582 First public use of ether, 1846	**16** Noah Webster, 1758–1843, compiled first American dictionary
17	**18** Alaska purchase, 1867	**19**	**20**
21	**22** Metropolitan Opera House opened in NYC, 1883	**23**	**24** United Nations Day
25 Johann Strauss, 1825–1899, famed composer	**26** Erie Canal opened, 1825	**27** Theodore Roosevelt, 1858–1919, 26th President—soldier, naturalist, awarded Nobel Peace Prize, 1906	**28** Statue of Liberty dedicated, 1886
29 Edmund Halley, 1656–1742, English astronomer, forecast orbit of Halley's comet	**30** John Adams, 1735–1826, 2nd President	**31** Halloween	

131

DO YOU KNOW YOUR SPIRITS?

In the month of Halloween, man's fancy turns to spirits. But to see a ghost is one thing and to identify him by his right name is definitely another. Your task here is match the names of a variety of ghosts and spirits with the respective thumbnail definitions of their specialties in the right column. Let your spirits guide you, otherwise you won't have a ghost of a chance. Get 11 or more correct matches, and you are 'SPIRIT'ually superb.

WHICH OF THESE SPIRITS . . . SPECIALIZES IN . . .

1. Kobold

a) Stealing children in mountainous regions?

2. Gremlin

b) Robbing graves and feeding upon corpses?

3. Leprechaun
4. Brownie
5. Vampire
6. Will-o'-the-wisp
7. Goblin

c) Being mischievous in the household?
d) Guarding mines and quarries?
e) Playing tricks upon aviators?
f) Entering and re-animating a dead body?
g) Assuming a living person's likeness shortly before his death?

8. Erlking

h) Performing good-naturedly helpful service at night?

9. Ghoul

i) Revealing, when caught, the hiding place of a treasure?

10. Banshee

j) Forewarning families, by wailing, of the approaching death of a member?

11. Zombi
12. Wraith
13. Troll

k) Haunting groves and grottoes?
l) Being particularly malicious to children?
m) Presenting itself in the form of dogs, serpents, even human beings?

14. Gnome

n) Misleading and misdirecting people in the open spaces?

15. Jinni

o) Sucking the blood of the living while they sleep?

132

COMPETITIVE WORD GAMES FOR ALL

THE SHORT WORD WINS!

Find the *shortest possible* word by adding as FEW letters as possible to *each* side of each letter pair. (No S-endings or proper nouns!) Example: 2. bOAr. Score 1 point for each letter added. 10 points if you are unable to make up a word. In some instances you will be able to find a word shorter than the answer provided. PAR SCORE is 25 points.

1. _____C Y_____
2. _____O A_____
3. _____L D_____
4. _____U S_____
5. _____M U_____

6. _____B B_____
7. _____U M_____
8. _____S U_____
9. _____D L_____
10. _____A O_____

THE LONG WORD WINS!

Find the *longest possible* word that can be spelled from the letters in each of the words below. Score as many points for each word as it has letters. Example: 1. Get the word BALMY from the word CYMBAL and score 5 points for it. In some instances you will be able to make a word longer than the answer provided. PAR SCORE is 66 points.

1. _____ CYMBAL
2. _____ ORCHID
3. _____ LUCERNE
4. _____ UNCLEAR
5. _____ MARINERS

6. _____ BEHAVIOR
7. _____ USURPATOR
8. _____ STRENUOUS
9. _____ DEDICATION
10. _____ ABSORPTION

HIDDEN WORDS

Add and subtract the letters in the names of the pictures shown below. Do everything correctly and you may discover something new.

INTERNATIONAL DOUBLE-TALK—IN PLAIN ENGLISH

You will find here the definitions of some common English phrases consisting of two words. The last half of these words is supplied, you are asked to find the missing first word which—in every instance—means pertaining to a foreign country. Example: 1. *French* Leave. A score of 20 or more is excellent.

1. A hurried informal leave-taking is a _____LEAVE
2. A mayonnaise dressing with a pungent addition is _____DRESSING
3. A time that will never, never come is called _____CALENDS
4. A small green and brown leaf chafer is a _____BEETLE
5. A bitter bark containing quinine is the _____BARK
6. False courage excited by drinks is _____COURAGE
7. Paprika, the pungent fruit of the bonnet pepper, is _____PEPPER
8. A water-raising wheel is called a _____WHEEL
9. An alloy of copper, nickel, and zinc is _____SILVER
10. A scaly insect whose body yields a red dye is a _____BERRY
11. Hot cheese served on toast or crackers is called _____MONKEY
12. A bath where sweating is induced by hot air is a _____BATH
13. An oblong paving block, usually of granite, is a _____BLOCK
14. A felt-lined box used for cooking purposes is a _____STOVE
15. A rich pastry of dough raised with yeast is _____PASTRY
16. Craftiness in intrigue goes by the name of fine _____HAND
17. Something extremely intricate is called a _____PUZZLE
18. A large kind of jellyfish found in mid-ocean is a _____MAN-OF-WAR
19. A ballot guaranteeing compulsory secrecy is an _____BALLOT
20. A person with a black eye is said to have been to a _____WEDDING
21. An ice of egg white, rum, and lemon juice is a _____PUNCH
22. A plant with sword-shaped leaves is a _____BAYONET
23. Severe and oppressive servitude is called _____BONDAGE

24. A system of exercise of muscles and joints is   _____MASSAGE

25. A thin sheer fabric with raised dots is   _____MUSLIN

26. Nutritious starch obtained from the bitter cassava is   _____ARROWROOT

27. A leguminous forage plant goes by the name of   _____CLOVER

HOW # ARE YOU AT 𝄢 LANGUAGE?

The world of signs and symbols is truly ONE WORLD for scientists, doctors, musicians, and other professional men in many fields where language is no barrier. For the sake of this quiz we have employed some of the more common signs and symbols used in some imaginary phrases that may have been uttered by various representatives in the United Nations. There is really nothing to guess here. If you can read the phrases you've scored very well already.

1. Let me ▬ my statement that our aspirations in # research are entirely peaceful ones.

2. There does not seem to be the slightest Ⴊ in the mind of the distinguished representatives to use the ☉ as a vantage point for military surveillance of the ⊕.

3. There is no ▬ for men of good will to at least try to better the lot of all people, ♂ and ♀.

4. Ɍₓ my word for it: we have ┼ proof that this country's military strength ⟋ than admitted here.

5. There is not an Ȝ of truth in what has just been heard.

6. So it seems that our aim is the same and there is a ᔕ only in the methods employed.

7. The ℘ to our well intentioned proposals should bear in mind that we are determined not to let anybody ₦ in the internal affairs of this country.

8. Let us take the evil by the √ and listen to the ⅄ of all peace loving nations to ☐ this dispute once and for all.

9. Although the ° of the world's ills seems staggering it seems ♮ for all of us to carry on as best as we can.

10. To Σ up all that has been said I prefer to believe that a ⸮ for the better has taken place.

ODD DISH OUT!

In each of the groups of courses printed on the menus below there is one item which, for reasons of culinary logic, does not fit. The CREAM PUFFS, for instance, are small cakes and do not belong into the group 1. of APPETIZERS. Spot 10 or more ODD DISHES (or drinks) and you have achieved culinary culmination!

1) Crabmeat Cocktail
   Sardine Canapes
   Piquant Puffs
   Cream Puffs
   Caviar

2) Sally Lunn
   Pretzels
   Petits Fours
   Zwieback
   Pumpernickel

3) Pilsen
   Ale
   Julep
   Stout
   Porter

4) Lobster Bisque
   Biscuit Tortoni
   Petite Marmite
   Bouillabaisse
   Bouillon

5) Artichokes
   Kumquat
   Kohlrabi
   Squash
   Succotash

6) Charlotte Russe
   Surprise Balls
   Lyonnaise Potatoes
   Pommes Frites
   Potatoes Anna

7) Oyster Rarebit
   Tilefish
   Lobster Thermidor
   Bullhead
   Mock Crab

8) Turkey
   Pheasant
   Quail
   Hasenpfeffer
   Venison

9) Goulash
   Chili con carne
   Sauerbraten
   Spareribs
   Short Ribs

10) Partridge
    Chicken
    Squab
    Goose
    Duck

11) Peaches Melba
    Marron Glace
    Spumoni
    Baked Alaska
    Lalla Rookh

12) Floating Island
    Snow Pudding
    Date Whip
    Yorkshire Pudding
    Swiss Rice

13) Timbale
    Welsh Rarebit
    Roquefort
    Brie
    Camembert

14) Bordeaux
    Moselle
    Claret
    Burgundy
    Tokay

15) Pousse-café
    Benedictine
    Cognac
    Chartreuse
    Curacao

FROM SOUP TO NUTS AND BEYOND

No fancy foreign words on this menu but puzzling, nevertheless. For we have substituted other definitions for the words that make up this tasty menu. How many courses can you decipher?

1. harbor   2. straphangers   3. kind of fog   4. easy task
5. grope for   6. terrible actor   7. gripe
8. fret   9. name lists   10. Georgians   11. urges on
12. severe pressure   13. callus   14. grows fast
15. enjoy   16. afternoon party   17. compact mass   18. phony praise
19. lunatics   20. gems

A HUNGRY MAN!

Help Mr. Jones get home while the turkey is still hot. Start at any of the colored dots.

THE PROBLEM OF THE WIRY MEN

Can you pair the nine wiry men with the respective objects they can be associated with? If so, the letters listed in order of the objects will spell out what they all (except one, maybe) have in common.

AUTOMOBILE
BICYCLE
CANOE
TRACTOR
ROCKET
SKATES
SKIS
SLED
SLEEPING CAR

RIDDLES, RIDDLES, RIDDLES

1. What happens to little girls who eat bullets?
2. What makes a road broad?
3. What is the best butter in the world?
4. Three girls walk to school under one umbrella. Why didn't any of them get wet?
5. What's the difference between an old dime and a new penny?
6. What animal has the head of a cat, the tail of a cat, the way of a cat, and yet isn't a cat?
7. What is the best thing to put into pies?
8. When do we have four hands?
9. Why did the man stand in back of a mule?
10. Why did the house call for a doctor?
11. What always has an eye open but never sees anything?
12. What is it that you must keep after giving it to someone else?
13. What kind of coat is made without buttons and put on wet?
14. How do you know that a bowling alley is always quiet?
15. What do you have in your possession that is most useful when it is used up?
16. If you put three ducks into a crate, what would you have?
17. When is a black dog most likely to enter the house?
18. What flower grows between your nose and your chin?
19. Why is the sea so restless?
20. What is a good example of wasted energy?
21. How many wives is a man given by the minister in the marriage service?

SHAPES IN NATURE

Here are 6 sets of things in nature with 3 names in each set. Each silhouette shape represents a member of one of the sets. Match each shape with the proper name.

1. Mountain
   Butte
   Mesa

2. Crab
   Octopus
   Lobster

3. Ostrich
   Guinea fowl
   Pelican

4. Africa
   Australia
   South America

5. Ant
   Spider
   Ladybug

6. Armadillo
   Raccoon
   Panther

ACTORS ANONYMOUS

Each of the actors below is studying the part he thinks he is best suited for. Each is imitating one of the world's most famed or infamous persons of fact and fiction. Can you identify them by name from their costumes and then match them with the thumbnail description of their deeds (or misdeeds) listed below in mixed order. A score of 10 or more qualifies you for a leading role.

A) Fighting against windmills
B) Looking for an honest man
C) Being first in San Salvador
D) Taking on the Hound of the Baskervilles
E) Burning Moscow
F) Robbing the rich to help the poor
G) Liberating Switzerland

H) Burning Rome
I) Starting a World War
J) Writing the *Divine Comedy*
K) Revenging his father
L) Judging the "fairest of all women"
M) Crossing the Rubicon
N) Fighting innumerable duels

WHAT GOES ON IN THE LETTER CIRCLE?

For an explanation of how to solve this puzzle best, please turn to page 17.

FOR YOUNGSTERS	FOR PARENTS
A) Tree trunk	A) Yellow
B) President Rutherford	B) Man of loincloth fame
C) Noise	C) _____, Sir
D) Playwright Eugene	D) Stadium sound
E) Affirmative votes	E) Exclamation
F) Simple affirmative	F) "The Divine"
G) Garfield's successor	G) Extinct monster in short
H) Sick	H) One of the Websters
I) Perform	I) French winter
J) Toss	J) Those in favor
K) Exclamation of surprise	K) "The Swedish Nightingale"
L) Bee house	L) Kind of apple
M) Man of the Ark	M) Deer
N) Conjunction	N) Well _____
O) Indian leader	O) Guiseppe
P) Mowed grass	P) _____ Carlos: Work of above
Q) Put on	Q) Record
R) Italian composer	R) Chester
S) Dexterity	S) Eugene
T) Cheer	T) Throw
U) Jenny _____: Songstress	U) Ace
V) Opposite to rare	V) One vote winner
W) Jacob's wife	W) Bad
X) Weekday: Abbreviation	X) Lew Wallace hero
Y) Ben _____	Y) Tree
Z) A	Z) Altar

141

FAMILY QUIZ GAME

For an introduction to this popular *Parents' Magazine* FAMILY QUIZ GAME please turn to page 18.

FOR MOTHERS

WARDROBE

(1) Give the name of the full, loose dress named after a Mother Goose character. (2) From what animal do we get mohair? (3) True or false: Dacron is a synthetic fiber. (4) What is the sash called that is worn with the kimono in Japan? (5) Who designed the topless bathing suit? (6) What is high fashion called in French? (7) What color is ecru? (8) If you were wearing Mary Janes, what would you have on? (9) Where did the middy blouse get its name? (10) What is the proper name for a monk's hood?

FOR FATHERS

SCIENCE

(1) The chemical symbol of iron is _____ . (2) A substance which accelerates a chemical reaction but which can be recovered at the end of the reaction is often called a _____ . (3) Name the device which supplies steady electrical impulses to the heart, in order to keep it beating evenly? (4) What substance gives blood its red color? (5) What is measured by amperes? (6) Are infrared rays invisible? (7) The science that deals with insects is called _____ . (8) Earthquakes are measured by an instrument called a _____ . (9) Who was the father of cybernetics? (10) The chamber, with a lever at one end, in which mice are placed for psychological experiments, is called a _____ .

FOR YOUNGSTERS (5–6 YEARS)

FAIRY TALES

(1) True or false: Rip Van Winkle slept for 20 years. (2) What bird did the ugly duckling become? (3) In what story does the Queen ask, "Mirror, mirror on the wall, who is the fairest one of all?" (4) From what did the Fairy Godmother make Cinderella's coach? (5) Whose garden was Peter Rabbit chased out of? (6) The character who befriends a lion by taking a thorn from his paw is _____ . (7) What is the name of Snow White's sister? (8) In the "Wizard of Oz," what character wanted a heart? (9) Who fell asleep at the Mad Hatter's tea party? (10) Who won the race between the tortoise and the hare?

FOR JUNIORS (6½–9 YEARS)

SPORTS AND GAMES

(1) The team game played on horseback with a ball and mallets is _____ . (2) What game is played on a diamond? (3) The center of a target is called the _____ . (4) True or false: A baseball team has more players than a basketball team. (5) How many players are there on a football team? (6) In tennis, what does "love" mean? (7) In what game is there a player called shortstop? (8) What is a southpaw pitcher? (9) If you are doing the crawl, you are a. skating b. swimming c. skiing. (10) The covering of an official baseball is made of _____ .

FOR PRE-TEENS (10–12 YEARS)

PRESIDENTS

(1) Monticello was the home of which President? (2) In what century was Calvin Coolidge President? (3) What famous speech begins "Four-score and seven years ago". (4) What was George Washington's home called? (5) Abraham Lincoln was born in what state? (6) True or false: The President has the power to declare war. (7) Who shot Abraham Lincoln? (8) Nixon was Vice-President when _____ was President. (9) Who was the 5th President of the U. S.? (10) True or false: President Kennedy was Governor of Massachusetts before he became President.

FOR YOUNG TEENS (13–15 YEARS)

ANATOMY

(1) What are auricles and ventricles? (2) The olfactory nerve is the nerve of a. taste b. hearing c. smell. (3) True or false: The main function of the white corpuscles is to fight infection. (4) Three bones called the hammer, the anvil, and the stirrup are located in the a. elbow b. foot c. ear. (5) The carpus is the a. collarbone b. elbow c. wrist. (6) Oxygen enters the body through the a. heart b. lungs c. stomach. (7) The study of biological cells is called _____ . (8) There are two main types of muscles in the human body, voluntary and _____ . (9) For what is a stethoscope used? (10) The retina is part of your a. eye b. ear c. nose.

STATE THOSE STATES

Arkansas is the best state to be in during a flood because its abbreviation is ARK. And Illinois is the unhealthiest state to be in because its abbreviation is ILL. With these examples in mind, see if you can answer the following questions with the proper state abbreviations.

1) Which is the most egotistical state?
2) Which is the cleanest state?
3) Which is the father of states?
4) Which is the doctor's state
5) Which state never fails?
6) Which is the Mohammedan state?
7) Which is the mining state?
8) Which is the state of exclamation?
9) Which state is the most Freudian?
10) Which is the most musical state?
11) Which is the most Catholic state?
12) Which state has the poorest marksmen?

PALMARY LOGIC

Can you, by employing sheer logic, arrange these 8 pictures in their correct order?

144

NOVEMBER

CALENDAR OF MEMORABLE DATES

1	**2** Daniel Boone, 1734–1820, frontiersman	**3** William Cullen Bryant, 1794–1878, American poet	**4**
5 Guy Fawkes Day—anniversary of the plot to blow up the Houses of Parliament in England, 1605	**6**	**7** Marie Curie, 1867–1934, co-discoverer of radium in 1898 Russian Revolution proclaimed, 1917	**8** Election Day
9	**10** Martin Luther, 1483–1546, founder of Protestantism U.S. Marine Corps created, 1775	**11** Veterans' Day	**12**
13 National Children's Book Week begins Robert L. Stevenson, 1850–1904, author of "Treasure Island"	**14** Robert Fulton, 1765–1815	**15** Articles of Confederation adopted by Continental Congress, 1777 Pike's Peak discovered, 1806	**16** Oklahoma, the 46th state, admitted to the Union in 1907
17 First session of Congress held in Washington, D.C., in 1800 Suez Canal opened in 1869	**18** Louis Daguerre, 1789–1851, invented first practical photography	**19** Gettysburg Address, 1863	**20**
21 Phonograph invented by Thomas Edison, 1877	**22** La Salle, 1643–87, French explorer, first to explore Mississippi to its mouth	**23** Franklin Pierce, 1804–69, 14th President of the U.S.	**24** Thanksgiving
25 Andrew Carnegie, 1835–1919, pioneer steel maker	**26**	**27**	**28**
29 Louisa May Alcott, 1832–88, author of "Little Women" and other stories for children	**30** Winston Churchill, 1874–1965		

145

IS IT 'PRESIDENT'IALLY POSSIBLE?

Here we are taking you on a 'quiz-it' to an imaginary museum displaying presidential curios. Decide which of the items mentioned here must be fake and state why.

If you can identify the true nature of the majority of all items on display you have a good chance to become the curator of the presidential museum.

WHICH OF THESE ITEMS MUST BE FAKE?

1. A button from a British uniform worn by George Washington.
2. Dwight Eisenhower's hand-written refusal to consider a third term.
3. A postage stamp commemorating the 100th birthday of John Adams.
4. The fountain pen with which Franklin Roosevelt signed the Atlantic Charter.
5. A personal letter from the king of Siam to Lincoln offering elephants as a war aid.
6. A newspaper clipping announcing the simultaneous deaths of two former presidents.
7. A photograph of Lincoln as postmaster in Salem.
8. A letter from a president to his father, a former president.
9. A police commissioner's badge in the name of Theodore Roosevelt.
10. A newspaper front page, dated November 7, 1948, headlining the defeat of Harry Truman.
11. The two pistol bullets which killed President McKinley.
12. A skin of a tiger shot by Theodore Roosevelt during a hunting trip to East Africa.
13. The autographed baseball with which Chester Arthur opened the season.
14. A friendship scroll addressed to Zachary Taylor signed by the Mikado.
15. A book shelf carpentered by James Garfield.
16. A black broadcloth coat made by Andrew Jackson.
17. The original ratified bill known as the Monroe Doctrine.
18. The marriage certificate of John Buchanan.
19. Woodrow Wilson's first draft of his opening address before the League of Nations.
20. Cleveland's personal thank-you note to the mayor for having named the city of Cleveland after him.

COMPETITIVE WORD GAMES FOR ALL

THE SHORT WORD WINS!

Find the *shortest possible* word by adding as FEW letters as possible to *each* side of each letter pair. (No S-endings or proper nouns!) Example: 2. dEAl. Score 1 point for each letter added, 10 points if you are unable to make up a word. In some instances you will be able to find a word shorter than the answer provided. PAR SCORE is 29 points.

1. _____V Y_____
2. _____E A_____
3. _____T D_____
4. _____E S_____
5. _____R N_____

6. _____A A_____
7. _____N R_____
8. _____S E_____
9. _____D T_____
10. _____A E_____

THE LONG WORD WINS!

Find the *longest possible* word that can be spelled from the letters in each of the words below. Score as many points for each word as it has letters. Example: 1. Get the word RIVET from the word VIRTUE and score 5 points for it. In some instances you will be able to make a word longer than the answer provided. PAR SCORE is 68 points.

1. _____ VIRTUE
2. _____ ENIGMA
3. _____ TORPEDO
4. _____ EPISTLE
5. _____ RICOCHET

6. _____ ARROGANT
7. _____ NAVIGABLE
8. _____ SPHERICAL
9. _____ DECORATIVE
10. _____ ASTROLOGIC

LOW BRIDGE, HIGH I.Q.

This truck driver is annoyed because his truck is just a half-inch too high to go through the underpass. He was about to turn back when he had a bright idea. Ten minutes later he was through the underpass and on his way. What did he do?

CAN YOU PAIR THEM FOR THE ARK?

If you were Noah and had the task of matching each of the animals in column A with another one in column B—how many such couples could you match correctly? Example: 1. ZEBU matches e) YAK both being OXEN of some kind. A score of 15 or more correct matches is very good.

A	B
1. Zebu	a) Brant
2. Grizzly	b) Shire
3. Aardvark	c) Basset
4. Capuchin	d) Manx
5. Tortoiseshell	e) Yak
6. Alpaca	f) Beluga
7. Gorilla	g) Pika
8. Gazelle	h) Teal
9. Onager	i) Mandrill
10. Flemish giant	j) Moray
11. Sulphur-bottom	k) Catamount
12. Clydesdale	l) Caribou
13. Coyote	m) Chimpanzee
14. Mallard	n) Wensleydale
15. Skye	o) Quagga
16. Southdown	p) Vicuna
17. Conger	q) Kodiak
18. Embden	r) Lobo
19. Cougar	s) Eland
20. Musk	t) Pangolin

SIGNS AND SYMBOLS

All that is needed here is to match the various symbols with the proper person listed in the left-hand column. Get 8 more correct and you get an A, the symbol for excellence.

ACCOUNTANT
ARCHITECT
ASTROLOGER
BANKER
CARPENTER
DRUGGIST
ELECTRICIAN
MAPMAKER
MUSICIAN
PRINTER

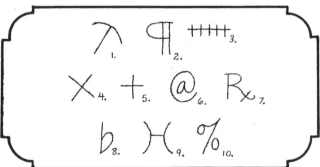

COW OR HORSE

The answer to each of the two-part questions below is either the HORSE or the COW. This gives you a fifty-fifty chance for the right answer without knowing anything about either animal but having learned something about both animals when you are through with the quiz. No city slicker you if you get 10 or more correct answers.

1 a) Which has two toes?
1 b) Which has one toe?

2 a) Which is angry when it paws with its forefeet?
2 b) Which is hungry when it paws with its forefeet?

3 a) Which seizes its forage with the tongue?
3 b) Which gathers food with the lips?

4 a) Which rises on forelegs first?
4 b) Which rises on hind legs first?

5 a) Which has one stomach?
5 b) Which four stomachs?

6 a) Which defends itself by goring?
6 b) Which defends itself by kicking?

7 a) Which does not sweat?
7 b) Which perspires easily?

8 a) Which uses teeth in fighting?
8 b) Which never uses teeth in fighting?

9 a) Which retracts ears when angry?
9 b) Which does not retract ears when angry?

10 a) Which rolls in the dust?
10 b) Which does not roll in the dust?

11 a) Which lies down to sleep?
11 b) Which often sleeps standing?

12 a) Which lies down fore parts first?
12 b) Which lies down hind parts first?

13 a) Whose lips are only slightly movable?
13 b) Whose lips are very movable?

14 a) Which has a smooth tongue?
14 b) Which has a very rough tongue?

15 a) Which lives 12–18 years?
15 b) Which lives 30–40 years?

HOW PRACTICAL ARE YOU?

Here is another test similar to those designed by psychologists for the preliminary screening of applicants for jobs demanding, among other things, sharp discernment and a grasp of practical facts. The questions that follow are simpler than those in the actual test but try your skill at them anyway. Mark A or B whichever you think is correct, and C when you think it makes no difference. Give yourself 1 point for each correct answer. A score of ten or more made in five minutes shows that you are very clear-minded and alert—well able to solve life's many practical problems.

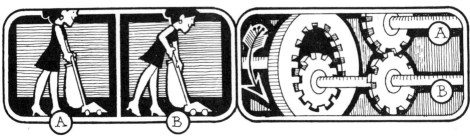

1. Which is the easier way of handling the vacuum cleaner?

2. Which cog turns in a direction opposite to the big cog?

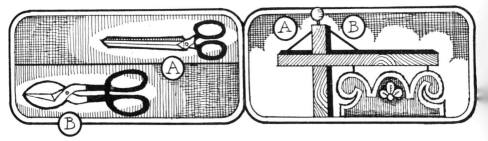

3. Which would be the better shears for cutting metals?

4. Which chain alone will hold up the sign?

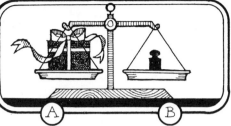

5. Which vase of flowers will tip over more easily?

6. Which weighs more?

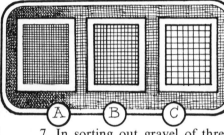

7. In sorting out gravel of three different sizes, through which sieve must the gravel pass first?

8. Which room has more of an echo?

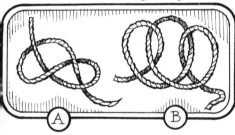

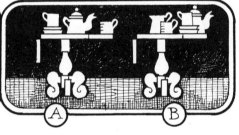

9. Which rope can be tied into a knot by pulling both ends?

10. Which table is more likely to break?

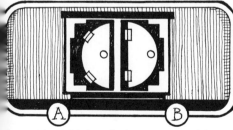

11. Which of these two cabinet doors would be easier to open?

12. Which man has the heavier load?

HOW QUICK-WITTED ARE YOU?

1. CLIMBING TO THE PEAK OF CONFUSION

A mountain climbing family was forced to proceed single file. In this way, the father was marching between a boy and a girl and the mother, likewise, between a girl and a boy. One boy walked between brother and father, a girl between sister and father, another girl between sister and mother, and finally another boy between mother and brother. Can you tell how many boys and girls there are and in what order the whole family is marching?

2. IT'S ALMOST IMPOSSIBLE!

How can you, by touching only one glass, make one row of glasses in which a full glass alternates with an empty one?

3. PERSONAL GET-TOGETHER

If you and me get together and don't care about orthography, we are a bird; if you and he get together you are a color. But if we and her get together it will be where? Or won't it?

4. A TOUCHY PROBLEM WITH TEETH

If the cog in the upper left corner is turned in the direction of the arrow, which two pieces will then touch on each other?

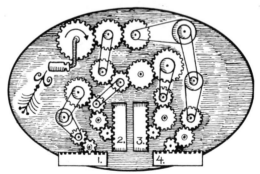

5. ELUSIVE LUCY

"Where is Lucy?" asked father
"She is not in the dining room," said mother.
"She is in the garden," declared John
"Yes, picking flowers," added Tom.
"No. she is in the attic," contradicted Mary
"That's not true," exclaimed Pat.
Can you tell where LUCY is if all statements except one are true?

6. MOVE A MATCH AND BE EQUAL!

By moving only ONE match in each of the equations, all can be made truly equal. How?

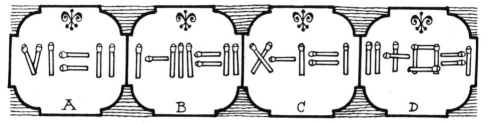

7. WHAT'S YOUR SCORE?

If somebody bets you that you cannot tell the score of some game before that particular game starts, would you be wise to take that bet?

THE TWINS' BIRTHDAY PROBLEM

Somehow the birthday gifts for the twins have gone awry. The same gift was to be given just once to each of the twins, but there are some gifts here in a single edition, while others appear more than twice. FIND THE ODD ITEMS!

WANTED: TWO MEN

If the police would request the citizenry to watch out for two men on their most wanted list and give the following descriptions of each of the men, could you spot the two criminals among the sixteen mug shots in five minutes?

MOST WANTED MAN A:

Square face
Small eyes
Long and straight nose
Small mouth
Small ears
Bushy eyebrows
Light, curly hair
Low forehead

MOST WANTED MAN B:

Oblong face
Big eyes
Long, straight nose
Wide mouth
Long ears
Medium forehead
Thin, arched eyebrows
Smooth parted hair

MUSICAL MESSAGE

Here is an urgent message in musical code. If you remember your scale you can sing right through this one.

Now, read the message:

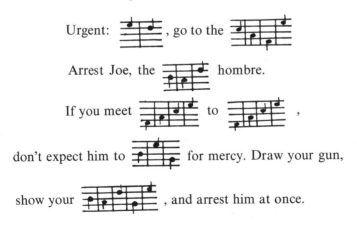

WHAT GOES ON IN THE LETTER CIRCLE?

For an explanation of how best to solve, this puzzle, please turn to page 17.

FOR YOUNGSTERS

A) Radium discoverer
B) Staff
C) Debark
D) Dragged
E) _____ Carnegie
F) Father
G) _____ Rogers: humorist
H) Resort place
I) Lincoln's nickname
J) Maude _____: actress
K) Peter _____: role of above
L) Mongrel dog
M) Arrest
N) Grizzly
O) _____ Air Force Base
P) Man's adornment
Q) First man
R) German reformer
S) Warrior of the Greek epic
T) Tumult
U) Barrier
V) Antelope
W) Animal food
X) Literary collection
Y) Sick
Z) King of Judea

FOR PARENTS

A) Contract
B) Historian
C) Nordic deity
D) Kodiak
E) Rogers
F) Peter _____
G) Sculptor
H) Collection
I) Martin
J) Madame _____
K) Leander's girl
L) Bridge
M) Literary cult
N) Carnegie
O) Spike
P) Ardor
Q) Actress
R) Drench
S) Archangel
T) Naturalist and explorer
U) Old _____
V) Ground
W) Saratoga Springs
X) Swiss canton
Y) Hoover
Z) Antelope

FAMILY QUIZ GAME

For an introduction to this popular *Parents' Magazine* FAMILY QUIZ GAME please turn to page 18.

please turn to page 18.

FOR MOTHERS:

WOMEN

(1) Who was the fair-haired heroine of Dickens' *A Tale of Two Cities*? (2) Queen Elizabeth was a member of what famous English family? (3) Who was known as the Maid of Orleans? (4) What's the name of John F. Kennedy's personal secretary who wrote a book about her years with him? (5) Who was the world's first woman Prime Minister? (6) Who was the first woman to fly a plane across the Atlantic? (7) Whose painted smile is famous? (8) What was the first American school established exclusively as a college for women? (9) Who was Uncle Tom's wife? (10) True or false: Wyoming was first to grant women the right to vote.

FOR FATHERS:

MYTHOLOGY

(1) Medusa, whose glance turned mortals to stone, was a _____ . (2) Who was condemned to the labor of bearing the world on his head and hands? (3) Who rules over Hades? (4) In Greek mythology, who was the first mortal woman? (5) Name an enchantress in Homer's Odyssey. (6) What was the name of King Arthur's legendary sword? (7) What Roman god had two faces? (8) The Greeks called their goddess of love _____ . (9) Who flew with wings of wax, but fell when they melted from the sun's heat? (10) Pan, Greek pastoral god, was part human and part _____ .

FOR YOUNGSTERS (5–6 YEARS):

NATURE

(1) Would it be more likely to snow in Maine or in Florida? (2) True or false: Leather comes from plants. (3) True or false: Plants absorb some of the water they need through their roots. (4) True or false: A spider's web is very strong. (5) Does an ocean contain fresh water or salt water? (6) If you wanted to boil water would you heat it or cool it? (7) Does oil come from the earth? (8) Does wool come from a plant or an animal? (9) A peninsula is surrounded by water on _____ sides. (10) True or false: In the winter the sun is seen during the day for a shorter time than during the summer.

FOR JUNIORS (6½–9 YEARS):

POSERS

(1) If your friend took your first name, and you took his last name, would you both have the same name? (2) If a clock struck once on the half hour and the number of hours on the hour, during what hour would it strike the same number at the hour and at the half? (3) Which is more: 9×4 or 5×8? (4) Unscramble these letters to spell a baseball team: DANSILCRA. (5) How much larger is a circle four inches in diameter than a circle two inches in diameter? (6) The plural of goose is _____. (7) Which number is smaller, one million or infinity? (8) Unscramble these letters to make a fruit: NLOEM. (9) Unscramble the fruit you found to make another fruit. (10) What relation is your father's sister to you?

FOR PRE-TEENS (10–12 YEARS):

WORDS

(1) "Braces" is another word for what article of clothing? (2) Which of these word pairs are not homonyms: a. meet, meat b. good, bad c. bear, bare? (3) A sentence has two parts, a subject and a _____ . (4) A hideous object is a. ugly b. pretty c. invisible. (5) The opposite of expand is _____ . (6) A gregarious person is _____ . (7) A _____ is often called a tar. (8) Which is correct: If I *were* you or if I *was* you? (9) Which of the following words is an interjection a. the b. great c. oh d. slowly? (10) Words that have the same meanings are called _____ .

FOR YOUNG TEENS (13–15 YEARS):

WAR

(1) Who was President of the Confederate States during the Civil War? (2) In what state is the famous Revolutionary War town of Lexington? (3) Who was the first great U. S. naval hero? (4) Who was President when the White House burned? (5) What country did Germany invade on Sept. 1, 1939? (6) Northern opportunists who went South after the Civil War were called _____ . (7) In what year was Pearl Harbor bombed? (8) In the Civil War battle between the Monitor and the Merrimack, which belonged to the North? (9) On what continent did the Boer War take place? (10) Who was defeated at the battle of Waterloo?

ICY LOGIC

Can you arrange the pictures in their logical order?

DECEMBER

CALENDAR OF MEMORABLE DATES

1	**2** Monroe Doctrine established in 1823	**3** Illinois, the 21st state, admitted, 1818	**4** Washington's farewell to his troops, 1783
5 Martin van Buren, 1782–1862, 8th President of U.S. Walt Disney, 1901–1966	**6** Joseph Conrad, 1857–1924, English novelist	**7** Pearl Harbor, 1941	**8** Eli Whitney, 1765–1825, inventor of the cotton gin
9 John Milton, 1608–74, English poet	**10** Emily Dickinson, 1830–86, poet Alfred Nobel, 1833–96, inventor of dynamite, created Nobel prizes	**11** Indiana, the 19th state, admitted, 1816	**12** Pennsylvania ratified Constitution, 1787 Washington, D.C., became seat of U.S. government, 1800
13	**14** Hanukkah—Jewish festival, called "The Feast of Lights" George Washington died, 1799	**15** The Bill of Rights was ratified by the states, 1791	**16** Boston Tea Party in Boston harbor, 1773
17 Wright brothers first successful flight at Kitty Hawk, 1903	**18** New Jersey ratified Constitution, 1787	**19** Tyrus (Ty) Cobb, 1886–1961, one of baseball's greatest players	**20** Louisiana Purchase, 1803
21 Winter Solstice	**22** John Newberry died, 1767, first to publish books for children, Newberry Medal named in his honor	**23**	**24** Peace Treaty ending War of 1812 signed by U.S. and England
25 Christmas	**26**	**27** Louis Pasteur, 1822–1895	**28** Woodrow Wilson, 1856–1924, 28th President, creator of League of Nations
29 First Y.M.C.A. established in Boston, 1851 Texas, 28th state, admitted, 1845	**30**	**31**	

159

MERRY CHRISTMAS!

Christ'mas (krĭs'măs; krĭst'-), *n.* A church festival (Dec. 25) commemorating the birth of Christ.

This is Webster's definition of the 25th of December. But there is much more to Christmas. It is a custom filled with fact and fancy. In fact, the origin of Christmas is not limited to the Christian tradition, but can be traced back much further in time. Here is a sampling of questions connected with Christmas. Give your YES or NO answer and then turn to the answer page for further explanation.

A score of 15 or more correct answers is very good.

1. Christ was born several years before the year 1.   YES NO
2. The X in Xmas represents the cross.   YES NO
3. The Christmas tree made its first appearance in Germany. YES NO
4. Christmas Day has always been observed on December 25.   YES NO
5. Americans have celebrated the Christmas holiday ever since the first colonists came to America.   YES NO
6. The town of Santa Claus is in the State of Indiana.   YES NO
7. The General Grant Tree has been designated the Nation's Christmas Tree.   YES NO
8. The real Santa Claus (St. Nicholas, a 4th century bishop) came from Italy.   YES NO
9. The first tuberculosis Christmas seal or stamp was sold in the United States 50 years ago.   YES NO
10. St. Francis of Assisi was the first to set up a manger crib with the animals as part of the celebration of the Nativity. YES NO
11. The first Christmas card on record was sent during Washington's presidency.   YES NO
12. According to legend, the animals kneeling on Christmas Eve are cows and sheep.   YES NO
13. The use of mistletoe is not officially sanctioned by the Church.   YES NO
14. French children look in their shoes (not stockings) for presents.   YES NO
15. England's favorite sport on the day after Christmas is boxing.   YES NO
16. "Waits" were originally special church bells rung at Christmas.   YES NO
17. The Bible states that three kings came to rejoice at the birth of Christ.   YES NO
18. The use of holly as a decoration stems from Scandinavian customs.   YES NO
19. Scrooge is the main character in the poem " 'Twas the Night Before Christmas."   YES NO

COMPETITIVE WORD GAMES FOR ALL

THE SHORT WORD WINS!

Find the *shortest possible* word by adding as FEW letters as possible to *each* side of each letter pair. (No S-endings or proper nouns!) Example: 1. iCEd. Score 1 point for each letter added, 10 points if you are unable to make up a word. In some instances you will be able to find a word shorter than the answer provided. PAR SCORE is 36 points.

1. _____C   E_____
2. _____H   M_____
3. _____R   I_____
4. _____I   T_____
5. _____S   S_____
6. _____T   A_____
7. _____M   M_____
8. _____A   T_____
9. _____S   S_____
10. _____T   I_____
11. _____I   R_____
12. _____M   H_____
13. _____E   C_____

THE LONG WORD WINS!

Find the *longest possible* word that can be spelled from the letters in each of the words below. Score as many points for each word as it has letters. Example: 1. Get the word ORACLE from the word COALER and score 6 points for it. In some instances you will be able to make a word longer than the answer provided. PAR SCORE is 99 points.

1. _____COALER
2. _____HEROIC
3. _____RESCIND
4. _____INDULGE
5. _____SPECTRAL
6. _____TYRANNIC
7. _____MOONSTONE
8. _____ARABESQUE
9. _____SNAPDRAGON
10. _____TRANSIENCE
11. _____INSTIGATORS
12. _____MALINGERERS
13. _____EMANCIPATION

WHAT DO YOU REALLY KNOW ABOUT PEOPLE?

A well-known psychologist recently tested some of his contemporaries by using the question and answer game below. All you have to do is to answer YES or NO to the 20 statements, then turn to the answer page for the surprising solution.

1. Blond people are more reliable than brunet ones.
2. Obese people are more good-natured than others.
3. Unruly hair is a sign of unusual vitality.
4. A high, arched forehead is a sign of great intelligence.
5. Beautiful women are usually less intelligent than others.
6. An only child is usually a spoiled child.
7. Redheads have more temper than others.
8. A receding chin is always a sign of a weak will.
9. A prominent jaw on a person means strong will power.
10. Long narrow hands indicate artistic temperament and talent.
11. A person with small eyes is usually secretive.
12. Laughing a great deal makes a person fat.
13. People with small wrinkles around the corners of their eyes have a great sense of humor.
14. A very tall person is a 'born' leader.
15. If you stare at the back of a person's head he will turn around.
16. Someone who cannot look you in the eye is inclined to be dishonest.
17. People with buck teeth are scheming and/or vengeful.
18. A small mouth points to criminal tendencies.
19. Earlobes grown to the head point to character defects.
20. People with large feet are inclined to be wasteful.

"SCREEN" TEST

Following are three columns with 15 headlines in each column. Working from left to right, choose the one headline that would induce you to buy the newspaper. The answer page will reveal the results of this psychological "screen" test.

On the strength of these headlines—which paper would you choose?

A

1. WAR THREATENS
2. HEAT TO STAY
3. WEALTHY JEWELER ROBBED
4. SPORTS HERO NEAR DEATH
5. CANCER CONTROL NOT YET
6. ENVOY VISITS PRESIDENT
7. FLOOD THREATENS 100,000
8. HOLIDAY BUSINESS LAGS
9. FIREMAN FOILS SUICIDE
10. GERMS DEADLIER THAN BOMB
11. LIVING COSTS TO GO UP
12. ITALIAN PREMIER RESIGNS
13. OUR BOYS MAY LOSE TROPHY
14. MINE VICTIMS FEARED LOST
15. SENATE PASSES LAW

B

1. WAR-PEACE IN BALANCE
2. HEAT SETS RECORD
3. $50,000 GEMS STOLEN
4. SPORTS HERO SINKING
5. MOST CANCER STILL BAFFLING
6. PRESIDENT RECEIVES ENVOY
7. HEAVY FLOOD DAMAGE
8. BUSINESS BELOW LAST YEAR
9. SUICIDE SAVED BY FIREMAN
10. GERMS DECIDE FUTURE WARS
11. PRICES MAY RISE AGAIN
12. ITALIAN GOVERNMENT CRISIS
13. OUR TEAM HARD PRESSED
14. HEAR NOISE INSIDE MINE
15. LAW GOES TO PRESIDENT

C

1. STILL SEE HOPE FOR PEACE
2. SHOWERS???—MAYBE!!!
3. JEWELER HELD-UP IN HOTEL
4. SPORTS HERO FIGHTING FOR LIFE
5. SLIGHT PROGRESS IN CANCER CURE
6. PRESIDENT-ENVOY CONFER
7. RED CROSS SAVES FLOOD TRAPPED
8. LAST HOUR RUSH HELPS BUSINESS
9. CROWDS WATCH SUICIDE—SAVED
10. BOMB POWER LIMITED
11. NO PRICE DROP HELD LIKELY
12. FORM NEW ITALIAN GOVERNMENT
13. WE MAY STILL WIN TROPHY
14. ARMY SPEEDS MINE RESCUE
15. LAW PASSED BY HOUSE, SENATE

ELECTRIFY YOUR FRIENDS!

Some of the most astonishing of all science experiments are those that are performed with static electricity. If you walk across a thick rug on a cold, dry day and touch someone on the nose, a spark will often jump from your fingertip to his nose. This spark is static electricity on a tiny scale. Lightning is static electricity on a giant scale. And now stun your friends with these static electricity stunts.

THE STICKY CARD

Instead of shocking someone's nose, try this trick with a playing card. Hold the card in your hand and walk across the rug slowly, shuffling your feet as you go along. This will charge your body and the playing card with static electricity. Now place the card flat on the wall and take away your hand. The card will stick fast to the wall!

JUMPING SALT

Combing your hair with a plastic comb produces a strong charge of static electricity on the comb. Test this by making a small pile of salt on the table. If you hold the charged comb an inch above the salt, the grains will jump up and stick fast to the comb!

THE HUMAN BATTERY

One of the most striking of all stunts with static electricity is that of making a fluorescent light glow without connecting it to a current. Rub such a bulb briskly on your clothing and see it light up from the static charge that the friction produces! This experiment is particularly effective if you perform it at night in a darkened room.

THE HINDU ROPE TRICK

Here's another amazing comb stunt. Have you heard of the "Hindu Rope Trick" in which an Indian fakir makes a rope stand upright in the air with no visible means of support? You can actually perform this trick on a tiny scale!

Hold a piece of thread in one hand, and the charged comb an inch or so above it. The thread will stay rigid! If you move the comb around in small circles, the end of the thread will follow its movements in a very weird way!

THE PAPER ACROBATS

And now for the "Acrobatic Clowns"—a remarkable static trick that always fascinates everyone who sees it. You'll need a sheet of glass, two books about an inch thick, an ordinary cotton pocket handkerchief, and eight small paper clowns the same size as the one shown here.

You can use this picture as a pattern. Fold a sheet of paper three times, making eight thicknesses. Trace the clown on the folded sheet, then cut it out—cutting through all eight thicknesses at once. This will make eight little paper clowns.

Place the books flat on the table, about 6″ apart, and rest the glass across them. Put the clowns beneath the glass. Now rub the top of the glass briskly with the handkerchief. The paper clowns will start performing the most amazing acrobatic feats you ever saw! They will jump up to the glass, then back down to the table, turning every which way like real performers in a circus!

What makes the clowns behave like this? Rubbing the glass charges it with static electricity. This attracts the clowns upward. As soon as they touch the glass, however, they also become charged. Charged objects repel each other, so the clowns fall back to the table where they quickly lose their charge. Then everything starts all over again.

If you'd like to make a permanent toy out of the acrobatic clowns, tear a cover from a shallow cigar box, then cut a piece of glass the same size as the cover. Put the clowns in the box, and fasten the glass down with friction tape or adhesive tape around the sides.

The toy will last for many years. To make the clowns perform, all you have to do is rub the glass vigorously with a pocket handkerchief.

Remember that if at any time your clowns will not perform, it is only because of hot humid weather.

The first cold snap will cause your clowns to perform briskly.

A

B

C

D

E

F

G

H

I

J

K

L

M

N

O

P

Q

R

S

T

HOW STYLE-CONSCIOUS ARE YOU?

Represented by a table and a chair of the same style are the ten most common styles of furniture. Match each table with the chair of the same style. If you get 7 correct matches, you might consider work in interior decorating.

1. Early American (17th century)
2. Queen Anne (1690–1750)
3. Louis XV (1715–1774)
4. Chippendale (1750–1775)
5. Hepplewhite (most of 18th century)
6. Sheraton (around 1800)
7. Duncan Phyfe (1790–1820)
8. French Empire (early 18th century)
9. Regency (early 19th century)
10. Victorian (most of 19th century)

ARE YOU LETTER-PERFECT?

1. It's true that B follows A in the alphabet but what does it precede?
2. What has at least ten letters in it yet may have thousands at one time or another?
3. How can you tell anybody (including the boss) in just two letters what you think of him?
4. How, besides N-M-E, can you spell enemy in three letters?
5. There are many superstitions regarding an empty stomach and what one should (or should not) do, and the question now is: How safe is it to write a letter on an empty stomach?
6. Tell quickly which of the letters in Nixon are the same when reflected in a mirror.
7. Whether your name is Smith or Johnson it can be written in one single letter if you know how.
8. Take the first letter away from him, and he will remain unchanged; take his second letter, and he will still be the same; in fact, take his third letter and then the remaining ones and nothing will have changed him. Who is he?
9. There is a common English word of nine letters, RTH is the middle of it, short the beginning and the end of it. How do you spell this word?
10. Can you think of a five-letter word that is pronounced just like one of its letters?
11. This sounds ridiculously easy but can you tell in five seconds which four-letter word ends in ENY?
12. The anagram is an all-time favorite word puzzle. Test your skill with the following: (a) Tom can pet lions (b) Is it anger? No! (c) Accord I try not (d) Mend it in a tree.

HOW IS YOUR EYE FOR A MESS?

Casting a glance at his hobby room, the perplexed hobbyist here is looking for the one and only item that does not have at least one counterpart—excepting, of course, the people, the table, the walls, the door, and the floor. Can you spot this item?

WHAT GOES ON IN THE LETTER CIRCLE?

For an explanation of how to solve this puzzle best, please turn to page 17.

FOR YOUNGSTERS

A) Idle
B) Rubber manufacturer
C) Placed
D) State
E) Dynamite inventor
F) Fruit
G) Sound
H) First name in baseball
I) December 7 Harbor
J) Repose
K) Character
L) Behold
M) Whitney's invention
N) Help
O) Press for payment
P) Vegetable
Q) Diamond
R) Hail!
S) Nobleman
T) Christmas tree
U) Unity
V) Skill
W) Anger
X) Part of corn
Y) Burning
Z) Weight

FOR PARENTS

A) Aesthetic
B) Alfred
C) Anger
D) Communication unit
E) French victory site
F) Dismiss
G) Opera
H) Mauna _____
I) Elite
J) Portrait painter
K) asseverate
L) Silence
M) Rubber man
N) Harbor
O) Cobb
P) Eugene _____
Q) Cotton _____
R) Head
S) Put
T) Title
U) Horse
V) Weight in weight
W) Hungarian name
X) Asian mountain
Y) Hot
Z) Cake

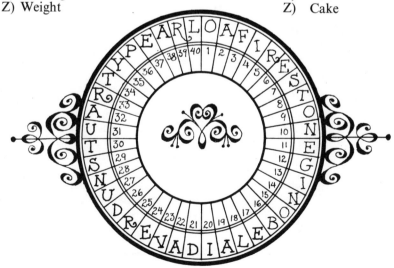

FAMILY QUIZ GAME

For directions to this popular *Parents' Magazine* FAMILY QUIZ GAME, please turn to page 18.

QUOTATIONS

(1) Where in the Bible do the words "Thy rod and Thy staff shall comfort me" appear? (2) True or false: An American colonial coin once bore the motto: "Mind your own business." (3) What famous playwright wrote the line: "Lord, what fools these mortals be!"? (4) What patriot described the American Revolution with the words: "These are the times that try men's souls"? (5) Who said: "Let us never negotiate out of fear but let us never fear to negotiate!"? (6) Who said: "Et tu, Brute!" in a play by Shakespeare? (7) Who said: "I only regret that I have but one life to lose for my country"? (8) What poet said: "If I can stop one heart from breaking, I shall not live in vain"? (9) Who said: "Good fences make good neighbors"? (10) The legendary "shot that was heard around the world" was fired where?

FOR FATHERS:

WORDS AND PHRASES

(1) What has the term "fourth estate" come to mean? (2) When you lie on your back, are you prone or supine? (3) A funambulist is a _____ . (4) What is the literal meaning of the word "veto"? (5) What does the phrase "ipso facto" mean? (6) What does the Latin phrase "pro tempore" mean? (7) A quack is to a physician as a pettifogger is to a _____ . (8) Alma mater is Latin for _____ . (9) What does "c" before a date mean? (10) To say the mind is, at birth, "tabula rasa" means _____ .

FOR YOUNGSTERS (5–6 YEARS):

TRANSPORTATION

(1) What do we call the seat for riding that is strapped onto a horse? (2) What makes a sailboat move? (3) The man who drives a railroad engine is called an _____ . (4) A wagon moves on wheels, but a sled moves on _____ . (5) The man who collects the tickets on a train is called a _____ . (6) Added together, how many wheels do a bicycle and a tricycle have? (7) A person who flies a plane is called an _____ . (8) How many wheels on a pair of roller skates? (9) What does the yellow traffic light mean? (10) What is the last car on a train called?

FOR MOTHERS:

FOR JUNIORS (6½–9 YEARS):

PLANTS

(1) Wine is usually made from what fruit? (2) What kind of trees do koala bears live on? (3) On what type of tree do coconuts grow? (4) What trees grow from acorns? (5) True or false: Strawberries have their seeds on the outside. (6) Which one of the following flowers grows from a bulb a. rose b. lily c. carnation? (7) What kind of trees are usually used for Christmas trees? (8) What grow in gardens but are not wanted? (9) What part of the carrot plant do we eat? (10) What is a "Chinese apple"?

FOR PRE-TEENS (10–12 YEARS):

UNITED STATES

(1) True or false: The U.S. did not enter World War II until two years after England and France entered. (2) Name the two U.S. cities with the largest population. (3) True or false: The U.S. has an ambassador in every country in the world. (4) True or false: "The Star-Spangled Banner" was written during the Revolutionary War. (5) True or false: The Pentagon is the world's largest office building. (6) Name the federal department which is responsible for the apprehension of nationally wanted criminals. (7) The first ten amendments of the Constitution are known as the _____ . (8) What legal document freed the American slaves? (9) Name as many states as you can that begin with "A". (10) True or false: The Navahos are the largest Indian tribe in the U.S.

FOR YOUNG TEENS (13–15 YEARS):

COMPOSERS

(1) Name the composer of *Peer Gynt*. (2) Name the composer of the *William Tell* overture. (3) Who wrote the *Unfinished Symphony*? (4) Who wrote the light opera *Iolanthe*? (5) . . . and "Peter and the Wolf"? (6) How many symphonies did Brahms compose? (7) Who wrote "The St. Louis Blues"? (8) "Old Folks at Home" and "My Old Kentucky Home" were written by _____ . (9) True or false: Mozart played the piano. (10) Who wrote the popular song "Blowin' in the Wind"?

A LITTLE LOGIC AMONG FRIENDS

I. Alf wears the same shirt as Fred and runs in a direction opposite to that of Dave. Dave wears the same cap as Carl whose hair is of the same color as that of Eric. Gus wears long pants. CAN YOU TELL WHO'S WHO?

II. Artur who speaks with Chas stands shoulder to shoulder against Bert whose hair is of the same color as Martin's. Lou does not smoke and Dan wears pants of the same material as Lou.
CAN YOU TELL WHO'S WHO?

ANSWERS

JANUARY

Page 8, **True Year—or False:** All Statements are True. Notes on the TRUE—FALSE Answers: 1) Up to 1752, Lady Day on March 25 was New Year's Day in English-speaking countries 2) In 1732, the Julian calendar was 11 days behind the Gregorian calendar, which was not adopted until 1752 4) Julius Caesar 6, 7) Years divisible by four are leap years only if they cannot be divided also by 100. If they can be divided by 400, however, they are leap years 10) After Pope Gregory XIII, who reformed the Julian calendar. **True Winter—or False:** 1) False: Extreme dry air makes heavy snowfall less likely because of the lack of moisture to form thick snow clouds. However, two-inch snowfalls have been recorded in temperatures of 20° below zero. 2) False: Siberia has recorded average temperatures of 90° against 60° on the South Pole. 3) True: It is estimated that heating raises the temperature from 1° to 4°. 4) False: Frost can be so intense as to blacken vegetation. 5) False: Due to certain regularities in the advance of a blizzard, it can be accurately forecast. 6) False: The coldest winter occurred in 1709 when the Adriatic Sea was frozen solid, while frost in Europe penetrated three yards into the ground. 7) False: The velocity of sound increases one foot per second for each degree of temperature as the temperature rises. 8) True. 9) False: The correct answer is 160,000,000 tons. 10) True: Hail forms only when a thunderstorm is going on, and this is a rare winter occurrence. 11) False: The shortest days are December 21, 22, 23. Until late in January the earth continues to give out more heat than it receives from the sun, thus warming the atmosphere. The coldest weather usually comes later. 12) True

Page 9, **Competitive Word Games for All** The Short Word Wins: 1) tHRow 2) krAAl 3) sPEd 4) sPYing 5) bYWay 6) aNEw 7) pENt 8) laWYer 9) tYPe 10) kEPt 11) krAAl 12) caRHop The Long Word Wins: 1) earth 2) rage 3) aspire 4) presto 5) grayed 6) uncles 7) venison 8) writers 9) strayed 10) seeping 11) rationale 12) chorines. **A Ducky Problem:** Like ducks and flowers 8 and 13; Like ducks and different flowers 5 and 14; Unlike ducks and same flowers 11 and 7.

Page 10, **Who's Who in the American City Directory:** 1k, 2n, 3s, 4m, 5t, 6q, 7u, 8x, 9y, 10w, 11v, 12r, 13p, 14o, 15i, 16j, 17l, 18g, 19h, 20b, 21c, 22a, 23e, 24d, 25f **Eye Q. Test:** The third and the fifteenth girls are alike.

Page 11, **'State'ly Words:** 1) SC ORE 2) IND IA 3) COLO NY 4) RI ME 5) IND ORE 6) LA ME 7) ME MO 8) CAL LA 9) ALA MO 10) PA ID 11) GA ME 12) FLA KY 13) LA VA 14) LA KY 15) O UT 16) MO DEL 17) FLA ME 18) LA TEX 19) LA ID 20) RI O 21) O VA 22) SC ALA 23) MO O 24) GA LA 25) RI GA 26) SC O UT. **The Activities of Señor Sombrero:** 1) mails a letter 2) rides bicycle 3) sells balloons 4) wearing skis.

Page 12, **No answers needed.**

Page 13, **Which Words Have All the Vowels:** 1) subordinate 2) unimportance 3) consultative 4) reputation 5) behaviour 6) veracious 7) equivocal 8) facetious 9) abstemious 10) gregarious 11) precarious 12) education 13) outdistanced 14) favourite 15) persuasion 16) authorized 17) precaution 18) unforgivable 19) perturbation 20) exculpation.

Page 14, **Associative Cancellations:** 1A) Bell-Telephone Inventor 1B) Hand 1C) Eve-Apple 1D) Lincoln-Famous Stove Pipe Hat 1E) Snow White-Dwarf 2A) Jill (of Jack and)-Pail 2B) Damocles-Sword 2C) Cupid 2D) Steeple 2E) Little Bo-Peep-Sheep 3A) Match 3B) Helen-Trojan Horse 3C) Siegfried-Dragon 3D) Columbine-Harlequin 3E) Key 4A) Edison-Electric Light Bulb 4B) Cinderella-Slipper 4C) Swan 4D) Jacob-Ladder 4E) Noah-Ark 5A) Romeo-Balcony 5B) Rembrandt-Painter's Palette 5C) Pandora-Box 5D) Wright Bros-Plane Inventor 5E) Tom, Tom the Piper's Son-Pig 6A) Diogenes-Lantern 6B) Daniel-Lion 6C) Ashtray 6D) Cleopatra-Pyramid 6E) Tent. Anagram: Haste Makes Waste 1B) Hand 2D) Steeple 3A) Match 3E) Key 4C) Swan 6C) Ashtray 6E) Tent.

Page 15, **Teasers and Posers for Young and Old:** 1) In alphabetic order. 2) The one occupied by the vertical strips: 13 small squares–if you divide the whole area into 25 small squares–against 12 for the horizontal strips. 3) 51 cubes. 4) Remove middle matches of the 4 outer sides and connect heavily ruled center lines, resulting in the loss of four but in the gain of 5 squares 5) 60%: 27% of the French speak no English, 13% of the English speak no French. Therefore, 40% speak only one language, the rest speak two. 6) The middle cube. 7) The 5 added must of course be added to the 7 removed, which makes a total of 12.

Page 16, **Are You a Game Detective:** 1)l Marbles 2)m Plane 3)j Swing 4)f Scooter 5)a

175

Top 6)k Seesaw 7)g Football 8)c Rattle 9)i Baseball bat 10)o Stilts 11)d Watering pot 12)e Slide 13)n Skipping rope 14)h Hula Hoop 15)b Bow and arrow. **The Number Game**:

$$23 \times 19 = 437 \qquad 39 \times 17 = 663$$
$$+ \quad + \quad - \qquad\qquad + \quad - \quad -$$
$$294 \div 3 = 98 \qquad 510 \div 5 = 102$$
$$\overline{317 + 22 = 339} \qquad \overline{549 + 12 = 561}$$

Page 17, **What Goes On in the Letter Circle**: For Youngsters: A) ALL B) ALLEN C) END D) TEST E) ANDREW F) NEW G) WATT H) LEND I) TAG J) STONE K) CAT L) RAN M) ONE N) IS O) NEST P) AGNES Q) TON R) AND S) DECATUR T) DREW For Parents: A) WATT B) NESTLE C) ST. AGNES D) ANDREW E) STONEWALL F) ATTEST G) STAG H) LEWIS I) ONE J) CAT K) UR L) NEW M) DREW N) TONE O) RAND P) ANDRE Q) WALL R) TON S) ALLEN T) DECATUR.

Pages 18–19, **Family Quiz Game**: FAMILY RELATIONS: (1) Hera (2) William Tell (3) Aunt Chloe (4) Guinevere (5) Claudia (6) Catherine (7) Tudors (8) Meg. Beth, Jo, Amy (9) 14 years (10) Mary Todd. PHILOSOPHY: (1) Stoics (2) Hedonism (3) Hegel (4) Logic (5) Bertrand Russell (6) Plato (7) Population (8) I think therefore I am (9) German (10) None–his method came to us through Plato. ANIMALS: (1) Yes (2) Pig (3) True (4) Turkey (5) White (6) Fawn (7) Ostrich (8) Lion (9) No (10) c. BIBLE: (1) Forty (2) Job (3) David (4) Slingshot (5) Adam (6) Garden of Eden (7) False (8) Moses (9) Joseph (10) Twelve. SPORTS & GAMES: (1) Battery (2) c (3) Umpire (4) True (5) Fifty-two (6) Seven (7) Rome (8) Baseball (9) Rook (10) George Herman Ruth. PHYSICS: (1) Water (2) Expands (3) Aurora borealis (4) Hydrogen (5) Nitrogen (6) 1.130 feet per sec. (7) CO_2 (8) Energy (9) South Africa (10) True **Ladybug**: The 4th and the 9th ladybug.

Page 20, **Are You on the Ball**: The scooter is violet. The lower light on the traffic light must be GREEN, as the car is just about to cross the street WITH the light. It follows that the upper traffic light is RED, which is corroborated by the fact that the Swiss flag also shows a white cross in a red field. The man calling to his wife in front of the shop window obviously refers to the two colors of the dresses as BLUE, and YELLOW, respectively. The tires on the motor scooter and cars are black, relating to the black section of the ball. Five colors on the boy's ball having been determined now as RED, GREEN, BLUE, YELLOW, and BLACK, it follows that the scooter must be of the sixth color shown on the ball. **A Dozen Dogs in One**: 1) Scottie 2) Pointer 3) Mastiff 4) Setter 5) Pekinese 6) Basset 7) Terrier 8) Spaniel 9) Beagle 10) Retriever 11) St. Bernard 12) Police

FEBRUARY

Page 22, **Love Is So Complicated**: A) 15–31 B) 10–28 C) 11–24 D) 1–27 E) 9–21 F) 17–33 G) 2–35 H) 18–29 I) 14–36 J) 13–26 K) 12–23 L) 3–20 M) 5–34 N) 16–22 O) 4–32 P) 8–25 Q) 7–30.

Page 23, **Competitive Word Games for All**: The Short Word Wins: 1) boGYman 2) dRAw 3) cODe 4) hUGe 5) sNOw 6) aDHere 7) witHDraw 8) tONe 9) aGUe 10) oDOr 11) hARe 12) oxYGen. The Long Word Wins: 1) begot 2) emigré 3) vector 4) listen 5) patching 6) coiled 7) spotty 8) obtains 9) steering 10) indicates 11) traitors 12) lackeys. **Planes in Collision**: 14 planes.

Page 24, **Job-Seeking Animals**: 1q, 2r, 3z, 4w, 5t, 6o, 7s, 8x, 9u, 10d, 11i, 12h, 13e, 14c, 15f, 16g, 17b, 18k, 19l, 20y, 21j, 22a, 23p, 24v, 25n, 26m. **Seafood from the Letter Fish**: Bass, Fluke, Pike, Pickerel, Cod, Eel, Mackerel, Flounder, Haddock, Crab, Shad, Perch, Smelt, Dace, Carp.

Page 25, **Animals Who Can Talk**: Fox, Drone, Chameleon, Wolf, Ape, Parrot, Shark, Dodo, Rat, Copperhead, Badger, Cat, Stag, Mouse, Sheep, Lion, Bear, Bull, Lamb, Tiger. **Can You Get Them into the Cage**:

L I O N	M I N K	G O A T	G U L L
L I M N	M I N E	C O A T	G A L L
L I M E	M A N E	C O S T	G A L E
L A M E	C A N E	C A S T	G A G E
C A M E	C A G E	C A S E	C A G E
C A G E		C A G E	

Pages 26–27, **No answers needed**.

Page 28, **Make a Match**: 1) D 2) G 3) J 4) T 5) P 6) R 7) K 8) Q 9) A 10) N 11) O 12) S 13) F 14) I 15) C 16) M 17) L 18) H 19) B 20) E

Page 29, **Riddles, Riddles, Riddles**: (1) At the bottom. (2) His left elbow. (3) It's too far to walk. (4) When it is scaled. (5) The spelling bee. (6) He keeps losing his skin. (7) Timetable. (8) They have so many fans. (9) A walking stick. (10) Glass. (11) Adam and Eve—they multiplied. (12) He was bald. (13)

The stalk brings them. (14) No, they had an apple. (15) A horseshoe nail. (16) He wanted to see the floor show. (17) One you lick with a stick; the other you stick with a lick. (18) Because you slip on both.

Page 30, **Eye Q. and I. Q.**: A) House B) Bicycle C) Trumpet D) Clock E) Cat F) Kite G) Birthday Cake H) Jack-o-lantern I) Head J) Tree K) Sunglasses L) Lollipop. **Two Rebuses for the Younger Set**: Rebus 1: BULB − LB + RECORD + NGI − BUG − CORN + SPOON − PRO = EDISON. Rebus 2: PARACHUTE + KN − TRUCK − EH − PAN + DIAL + MS − LI = ADAMS.

Page 31, **What Goes On in the Letter Circle**: For Youngsters: A) DYE B) ADAM C) CODY D) LAMB E) SELL F) GRANT G) EDISON H) ANT I) DAM J) RAN K) SONG L) TEN M) COD N) ELLA O) EL-LEN P) ABE Q) AD R) BE S) IS T) RICO U) DYED V) YE W) TENN X) TENNIEL Y) SO Z) BEAD. For Parents: A) BEAD B) ENRICO C) SELL D) GRANT E) ANTE F) SON G) TENNIEL H) CODY I) ANT J) LAMB K) DAM L) ABE M) ADAMS N) COD O) ELLEN P) SONG Q) EDISON R) TEN S) ELLA T) BABE U) ADA V) RANT W) DYE X) LAM Y) ELL Z) DAM-SEL.

Pages 32–33, **Family Quiz Game**: WOM-EN: (1) Rosa Bonheur (2) Duchess of Alba (3) "Silent Spring" (4) Madame, Señora, Frau (5) sob sister (6) Desdemona (7) "The Group" (8) Socrates (9) Mimi (10) Jenny Lind. WAR (1) Spanish Civil War (2) General Matthews (3) Havana Harbor (4) Arlington National Cemetery (5) Battle of Leyte Gulf (6) 1812 (7) Gettysburg and Vicksburg (8) c. China (9) true (10) England and France. COMIC STRIPS & TV: (1) The Bumsteads (2) Flipper (3) Captain Kangaroo (4) false (5) Jughead (6) Dogpatch (7) Walt Disney (8) Muskie and Vince (9) Clark Kent (10) Tonto. THE SKY: (1) Mars, Venus (2) false (3) moon (4) stars (5) winter (6) b. Jupiter (7) yes (8) true (9) Venus, Mercury (10) false. MUSIC: (1) guitar (2) brass (3) four (4) eight (5) piano (6) harmonica (7) "The Nutcracker Suite" (8) 18th (9) piano (10) two-C sharp and F sharp. ABBREVIA-TIONS: (1) United Nations International Children's Emergency Fund (2) Intelligence Quotient (3) National Labor Relations Board (4) Doctor of Philosophy (5) Amplitude Modulation (6) Intercontinental Ballistic Missile (7) North Atlantic Treaty Organ-ization (8) South East Asia Treaty Organization (9) National Recovery Administration (10) Atomic Energy Commission.

Page 34, **What Is Your 'View' point**: (1) B (2) D (3) C (4) B (5) C (6) C.

MARCH

Page 36, **How About Your Superstitions**: 1r, 2m, 3l, 4o, 5n, 6s, 7t, 8p, 9f, 10q, 11j, 12i, 13d, 14h, 15c, 16a, 17e, 18b, 19g, 20k.

Page 37, **Competitive Word Games for All**: The Short Word Wins: 1) eTHer 2) asHCan 3) vERy 4) dIAl 5) aDMit 6) dEFy 7) arSOn 8) pOSe 9) reFEr 10) duMDum 11) pAIl 12) bREw 13) aCHe 14) eigHTy. The Long Word Wins: 1) sluts 2) thatch 3) teaman 4) drains 5) inlaid 6) sealing 7) testament 8) bilious 9) infinity 10) induces 11) radiation 12) sensibly 13) culminating 14) mounters. **Relation'ships'**: Ship number 4 is the longest.

Page 38, **No Telling About Spelling**: 1) lead 2) tears 3) dove 4) entrance 5) wound 6) present 7) object 8) bow. **Mirror Magic**: There are only 3 persons.

Page 39, **How's Your Plurality**: 1) Theses 2) Aides-de-camp 3) Spokesmen 4) Notaries public 5) Châteaux 6) Francs-tireurs 7) Sheaves 8) Courts-martial 9) Moose 10) Tables d'hôtes 11) Opossums 12) Cocos 13) Enigmas 14) Attorney(s) generals 15) Rabbis 16) Fezzes 17) Governors general 18) Odea 19) Oxen 20) Bantu 21) Onyxes 22) Judge Advocates 23) John Dorys 24) Gentlemen's gentlemen 25) Jack-in-the-boxes 26) Hors d'oeuvres 27) Sheaths 28) Talismans 29) Potatoes 30) Brigadier generals 31) Species 32) Sons-in-law 33) Fifes 34) Genera 35) Finnan haddies 36) Jinn 37) Men-of-war 38) Autos-da-fé 39) If's 40) Cousins-german 41) Papyri 42) Normans 43) Mongooses 44) Musk deer 45) Hundredweights 46) Ignes fatui 47) Handfuls 48) Infant prodigies. **Hidden Words**: A + CORN − CAN + PAN + PIG + E − PIPE + E = ORANGE. X + FLOWER + I − FOX − R + MOP + H − WHIP + N = LEMON.

Pages 40–41. **No answers needed**.

Page 41, **Spot the Odd Ones**: 1)C–figure with even number of sides 2)D–'script type' P 3)C–card containing pips from *all* suits 4)A–circle containing 9 dots, all others have 11 5)B–domino containing 8 pips instead of 7 like the rest 6)C–Marine insignia, the others are army insignia 7)C–left eye in the set 8)D–"waning" moon in the set 9)B–not divisible by nine 10)B–not divided into 8 spaces but into seven.

Page 42, **Oh, These Anachronistic Artists**: 1) church–steeple and gothic arch 2) American flag 3) Clock 4) Antenna 5) Balloon 6) Electric lamp 7) Street sign (Main Street) 8) Tin can 9) Gun of soldier 10) Pipe 11) Clothes hanger 12) Bicycle 13) Camera 14) Newspaper 15) Toy car 16) Socks and sneakers on child 17) Tea pot and cup 18) Hat on lady in house 19) Baby bottle 20) Glasses on woman (on balcony) 21) Pencil 22) Ice cream cone 23) Roman arch

Page 43, **How Quick-Witted Are You**: 1) Strange Equation $45 - 5 : 4 = 10$
$$45 + 5 : 5 = 10$$
2) How Reflective Are You: 6:50 o'clock 3) A Weighty Woman: Candy 4) Whose Move Is It: Mr. WALKER—runs, Mr. RUNNER—rides, Mr. RIDER—hikes, Mr. HIKER—walks 5) Change Your Partners:

M W M W
W M W
W M
M

Page 44, **Animal Hunt in the Cities**: 1) ATLAN̲TA 2) OX̲FORD 3) ATH̲ENS 4) ROTT̲ERDAM 5) CLEVE̲LAND 6) MOS̲COW 7) DOVER 8) BUDA̲PEST 9) TAL̲LAHASSEE 10) BERNE 11) ASPEN 12) D̲AMASCUS 13) GARY 14) NE̲WTON 15) BALBOA 16) YAKIMA 17) ELKHART 18) MILW̲AUKEE 19) WHEELING 20) SAC̲RAMENTO. **A Square Problem**: 23 WHITE 22 BLACK tiles.

Page 45, **What Goes On in the Letter Circle**: For Youngsters: A) SUM B) BACH C) BROW D) ACHE E) HENRY F) BROWN G) THE H) BROWNING I) HEN J) ROW K) OWN L) ERA M) RAVE N) HER O) CAT P) ORB Q) HE R) ERE S) LUTHER T) UT U) ME V) OR W) GLUT X) AVE Y) RAVEL Z) RESUME. For Parents: A) CATO B) BACH C) ELBA D) MERCATOR E) BROWNING F) RÉSUMÉ G) HENRY H) MER I) ORB J) LUTHER K) BROWN L) RYDER M) CAT N) HEN O) RAVEL P) HERA Q) AVE R) ACHE S) BROW T) OWNING U) ERA V) SUMER W) SUM X) ROW Y) DERE Z) GLUT.

Pages 46–47, **Family Quiz Game**: HOME ECONOMICS: (1) 16 (2) the dark (3) before food or before the meal (4) flaxseed (5) a hand (6) let the buyer beware (7) eight (8) 32 (9) false (10) herb. LEADERS: (1) Yugoslavia (2) Mao Tse-tung (3) Burma (4) Cyprus (5) Stephen Douglas (6) Levi Eshkol (7) Gladstone (8) Nguyen Cao Ky (9) John Adams (10) Clement R. Attlee. NURSERY RHYMES: (1) fat (2) Georgie Porgie (3) jump over a candle (4) to school (5) your garden grow (6) in a pumpkin shell (7) a tuffet (8) laughed (9) their mittens (10) to market. BIRDS: (1) ostrich (2) bluebird (3) parrot (4) when frightened its cry sounds like that of a cat (5) a. hummingbird (6) eagle (7) penguin (8) penguin (9) ostrich (10) c. wings. CITIES: (1) false—Constantinople is the old name for Istanbul. (2) false—It is located in East Germany. (3) Wyoming (4) New York City (5) a. New York City b. Paris c. Berlin (6) Fenway Park (7) Venice (8) Kitty Hawk (9) Independence Hall, Philadelphia (10) Paris. FIGURING: (1) Sunday (2) multiply the width by the length (3) .3 (4) $6\frac{1}{4}$ (5) 176 (6) 75 cents (7) none (8) one (9) one hundred (10) arithmetical.

Page 48, **What Goes With What in the Picture Circle**: (1) glass with (2) barrel; (3) butter with (9) knife; (4) plant with (13) caterpillar; (5) tree with (18) squirrel; (6) cow with (20) milk; (7) bee with (16) honeycomb; (8) cheese with (15) mouse; (10) nutcracker with (11) nut; (12) acorn with (19) oak leaf; (14) rain with (17) umbrella.

APRIL

Page 50, **Classified Nonsense**: 1) The reckoning of years by B.C. started after the birth of Christ. 2) Tribes shrinking their enemies' heads are found only in South America. 3) There were no binoculars in Columbus' time. 4) 1894 was not a leap year, which makes a Feb. 29 date impossible. 5) Theoretically, a tripod is constructed so that it cannot wobble. 6) The statement itself is contradictory. 7) There is no Brazilian dollar. 8) George I was not George "I" while he reigned but became known as such only after his son George "II" succeeded him. 9) Sherlock Holmes is a fictional character. 10) The "pages" 37/8 can only be one page, as every odd-numbered page must be a right-hand page, the back of which would be page 38 here. 11) The smith never hits the anvil, as he can do so only when he *hears* the clock strike —a smith of iron cannot hear. 12) This is *not* true, as New Year's Day already belongs to the next year. 13) There is no "Secretary of Justice."

Page 51, **Competitive Word Games for All**: The Short Word Wins: 1) lAYer 2) sPAr 3) oRDer 4) fISt 5) aLLy 6) aFOul 7) pOOl 8)

178

lOFt 9) oLLa 10) aSIde 11) aDRoit 12) cAPa. The Long Word Wins: 1) bread 2) aspire 3) baiter 4) tearing 5) silence 6) arrant 7) coined 8) collates 9) wheeling 10) diluters 11) reactions 12) roasting.

Page 52, **What's in a Name**: 1) Sandwich–two slices of bread with a layer of meat, etc. between them. 2) Derby–a stiff felt hat. 3) Napoleon–a richly iced cake. 4) Wellington–a high boot. 5) Mae West–a yellow life saving jacket. 6) Annie Oakley–a free pass. 7) Macadam–broken stone for roadways. 8) Colt–a revolver. 9) Vandyke–a trim pointed beard. 10) Davenport–a large sofa or writing desk. 11) Mansard–a garret. 12) Pompadour–a high-rolled hairstyle. 13) Bowie–a hunting knife. 14) Vernier–a scale for computations. 15) Sally Lunn–a sweetened teacake. 16) Stanhope– a light open vehicle. 17) Gladstone–a long narrow traveling bag. 18) Diesel–a motor or engine. 19) Silhouette–a representation of an object's outlines. 20) Morse–a telegraph. **What's in the Letter Closet**: Boot, Beret, Belt, Busby, Cap, Collar, Coat, Glove, Sock, Trousers, Blouse, Overcoat, Robe, Scarf, Shirt, Shoe, Slipper, Skirt, Sweater, Tie, Vest, Jacket.

Page 53, **Test Your Relativity**: 1) fifth cousins 2) grandfather/daughter 3) none 4) son/father 5) brother/sister 6) mother/daughter 7) father/son 8) uncle/niece 9) none 10) none 11) father/son 12) sisters 13) grandfather/son 14) father/daughter 15) none 16) brother/sister 17) none 18) father/daughter 19) none 20) son/father 21) none 22) grandfather/son 23) none 24) brothers 25) half-brothers.

Pages 54–55, **No answers needed**.

Page 56, **Nice 'Handi'work If You Can Get It**: 1) Traffic cop 2) Orchestra conductor 3) Gardener with shovel 4) Piano player 5) Auto driver 6) Rifleman 7) Golfer 8) Roman Emperor's death signal 9) Hitchhiker 10) Baseball batter 11) Man driving nail into wall 12) Somnambulist.

Page 56, **Big Game Hunting**: The Tiger.

Page 57, **Riddles, Riddles, Riddles** 1) Because nothing gets in their hair. 2) Washington, D.C. 3) They move quickly. 4) He takes things easy. 5) Both have pitchers. 6) A bulldozer. 7) 40 pennies, 8 nickels, 2 dimes. 8) He heard they were having a new serial. 9) A window needs washing on both sides. 10) Because he was a light sleeper. 11) Bowling. You can hear a pin drop. 12) A centipede with corns. 13) A window. 14) Because he couldn't go under it. 15) With a knife and

fork. 16) Not a word. He was shocked by the whole thing. 17) Fruit salad. 18) Because the books were in tiers. 19) Bandits, of course. 20) A very high price to pay for corn. 21) A pigtail. 22) Because their father was an awful boar.

Page 58, **How's Your General Store of Information**: 1) Hanger 2) Hammer 3) Spoon 4) Book 5) Bottle 6) Pail 7) Soda glass 8) Light bulb 9) Frying pan 10) Envelope 11) Socks 12) Key 13) Cigar 14) Pencil 15) Clock 16) Ribbon 17) Box of matches 18) Candle 19) Hat 20) Cup 21) Eyeglasses 22) Teapot 23) Fountain pen 24) Knife 25) Spool of thread 26) Safety pin.

Page 59, **What Goes On in the Letter Circle**: For Youngsters: A) ERR B) PEARY C) EAR D) LENIN E) LEER F) TIT G) LEE H) TAN I) RIPE J) ALE K) TITANIC L) PEAL M) PEAR N) ICE O) REVERE P) PEA Q) NINA R) EVE S) TITAN T) NICER U) RIP V) ALEE W) ANTE X) EVE Y) ANT Z) NANTES. For Parents: A) ANTE B) LENIN C) NANTES D) EAR E) ESP F) PEALE G) TITANIC H) EVER I) ANI J) TIT K) PEARY L) PEAL M) YALE N) NICE O) ICER P) TITAN Q) TAN R) EVERETT S) LEER T) ALE U) LEE V) NINA W) ERR X) REVE Y) RIP Z) PEA.

Pages 60–61, **Family Quiz Game**: MEDICINE: (1) a. Skin (2) Hippocrates (3) No (4) b. Liver (5) Psychiatry (6) Orthopedist (7) No (8) High places (9) To measure blood pressure (10) Pancreas. SPORTS: (1) Jack Johnson (2) False (3) 60 (4) Dizzy Dean (5) Birdie (6) Jack Dempsey (7) Lou Gehrig (8) Puck (9) Red Grange of Illinois (10) Clay pigeons. FOOD: (1) d. Pig (2) True (3) Salty (4) Round (5) Fruit (6) True (7) Yellow (8) Little Miss Muffet (9) Christmas pie (10) Florida, California. THE SEA: (1) Pacific, Atlantic (2) Gulf of Mexico (3) School (4) Yes (they have no eyelids) (5) Water (6) Moon (7) Island (8) Arctic (9) False (10) True. THE BIBLE: (1) Joseph (2) Solomon (3) Samson (4) Moses (5) Passover (6) Sheba (7) Mount Sinai (8) Angels (9) Killing of the first-born (10) Joshua. MEANINGS: (1) Words and phrases that read the same backward and forward (Madam, I'm Adam) (2) Bridges (3) b (4) Always Faithful (5) Sovereign (6) An unfair arrangement of voting districts to favor one political party (7) Simultaneous attraction toward and repulsion from an object or person (8) True (9) With praise (10) Self-propelling vehicle.

Page 62, **A Cubist's Delight**: (1) 15 (2) 19 (3) 22 (4) 27 (5) 40 (6) 15 (7) 22 (8) 15 (9) 46 (10) 32 (11) 58 (12) 105.

MAY

Page 64, **Are You Motherwise**: 1) Mother earth 2) Mother country 3) Mother Goose 4) Mother of Parliaments 5) Mother tongue 6) Mother of Presidents 7) Mother-of-pearl 8) Mother Hubbard 9) Mother Superior 10) Mother of the Believers. **Do You Know Their Mothers**: 1) Hen 2) Sow 3) Ewe 4) Lioness 5) Jenny 6) Cow 7) Mare 8) Vixen 9) Cat 10) Nanny 11) Doe 12) Hind. **Ma's Without Sons**: 1) Aroma 2) Panama 3) Dogma 4) Gamma 5) Sigma 6) Stigma 7) Plasma 8) Magma 9) Panorama 10) Miasma 11) Lama 12) Drama 13) Cinema 14) Comma 15) Trauma 16) Coma 17) Enigma 18) Drachma 19) Alabama 20) Dilemma.

Page 65, **Competitive Word Games for All**: The Short Word Wins: 1) miSRead 2) oPEn 3) caRVe 4) pIEr 5) iNFer 6) eGGy 7) deaF-Ness 8) hEIr 9) liVRe 10) kEPt The Long Word Wins: 1) ghouls 2) platen 3) desire 4) drains 5) blouse 6) treading 7) turrets 8) bathless 9) negative 10) mushiest. **Looney Logic**. 1-E; 2-A; 3-D; 4-B; 5-C. The balloon bought by the girl appears in only one other of the scenes which must have preceded the buying scene. Hence the last picture E must be #1 of the logical sequence and the first picture A must be #2. Of the remaining three scenes, scene D shows the most balloons (15), indicating that the replenishing of stock took place at this point; scene B is the next to the last scene because there are 14 balloons against the 13 seen in the last scene C. The last balloon sold is the one with the black triangle which figures in all but the last scene.

Page 66. **Damsel in Distress**:

Page 67, **Flowery Answers**: Bittersweet, Baby's breath, Boxwood, Forget-me-not, Morning glory, Cowslip, Foxglove, Bachelor's button, Buttercup, Cockscomb, Jack-in-the-pulpit, Larkspur, Snapdragon, Bluebell, Lotus, Sweet William, Everlasting, Heartsease, Carnation, Wallflower. **Flower Bridge**: 1(e) MAR I GOLD 2(i) EVE R-LASTING 3(h) COW S LIP 4(k) FOUR O CLOCK 5(r) FLY T RAP 6(n) BUTTE R-CUP 7(l) HARE B ELL 8(c) HAW T HORN 9(s) FOX G LOVE 10(a) OR C HID 11(o) LO T US 12(b) SNOW B ALL 13(g) TUB E ROSE 14(f) DO G WOOD 15(q) COCK S COMB 16(j) DROP W ORT 17(d) I R IS 18(t) MONK S HOOD 19(m) CAM O MILE 20(p) SUN F LOWER.

Pages 68–69, **No answers needed**.

Page 70, **What's the Game**: A) Hopscotch B) Tennis C) Football D) Shuffleboard E) Croquet F) Basketball G) Baseball H) Ice Hockey I) Badminton J) Lacrosse K) Bowling L) Soccer ball M) Squash N) Field Hockey O) Rugby P) Volleyball.

Page 71. **Scrambled Calling Cards**: 1) Portrait Photographer 2) Marriage Broker 3) Patent Attorney 4) Editor & Publisher 5) Private Detective Agency 6) Exterminators & Fumigators 7) Magician & Conjurer 8) Psychiatrist & Psychoanalyst. **An 'Ess'ential Problem**: 12

Page 72, **Where Would You Meet These People**: 1) New Zealand 2) Peru 3) Philippines 4) United States 5) Siberia (U.S.S.R.) 6) Mexico 7) Algeria-Tunisia 8) Belgium 9) New Guinea 10) Siberia-Turkestan (U.S.S.R.) 11) Ceylon 12) China (Manchuria) 13) Hawaii 14) Hungary 15)Zanzibar (Africa) 16) Borneo 17) Turkmenistan (U.S.S.R.) 18) Chile 19) Northern Scandinavia (Sweden, Norway, Finland) 20) Ethiopia (Africa) **The Number Game**:

876 ÷ 12 =	73		312 ÷ 12 =	26
−	+	+	−	+	+
197 × 3 =	591		54 × 4 =	216
679 − 15 =	664		258 − 16 =	242

Page 73. **What Goes On in the Letter Circle**: For Youngsters: A) MAN B)TRUMAN C) BROWN D) BROWNING E) SEW F) DEN G) GOLDEN H) NOME I)SEWARD J) SOB K) RUM L) BASE M) MELBA N) OLDEN O) ELBA P) OLD Q) ANNOY R) BROW S) WARD T) UN U) WAR V) ANNO W) OWN X) MANN Y) ROW Z)

DUN. For Parents: A) MELBA B) SOB C) BROWNING D) GOLDEN E) ANTRUM F) BROW G) SEWARD H) NOME I) OLDEN J) MANN K) DEN L) GOLD M) DUNANT N) BROWN O) ANNOY P) TRUMAN Q) DUN R) ANNO S) ELBA T) SEW U) WAR V) ROW W) BASE X) OLD Y) WARD Z) OWN.

Pages 74–75, **Family Quiz Game**: NOVELS: 1) Henry Fielding 2) Sinclair Lewis 3) *Camille* 4) *Bonjour Tristesse* 5) *The Good Earth* 6) *Oliver Twist* 7) Napoleon 8) Henry James 9) *Ship of Fools* 10) *Grapes of Wrath*. SPACE: 1) true 2) northern lights 3) Surveyor 4) Jupiter C 5) b 6) approximately 150 miles 7) the mean distance from the earth to the sun 8) apogee 9) gaseous 10) Cape Canaveral. MUSIC: 1) accordion 2) do, mi 3) "Over the Hills and Far Away" 4) Old King Cole 5) yell 6) false 7) toes 8) false (at bedtime) 9) cello 10) a magician performs tricks and a musician plays music. FAMOUS PEOPLE: 1) pioneer 2) Benjamin Franklin 3) b 4) Dwight 5) in oil 6) Secretary-General 7) Peter Stuyvesant 8) a 9) Rubicon 10) Washington. MYTHOLOGY: 1) snakes 2) horse 3) chief of the Olympian gods 4) Atlas 5) Mercury 6) Eos 7) Cupid 8) Launcelot 9) Camelot 10) Romulus and Remus. MINERALS: 1) mercury 2) it supplied the keys to deciphering hieroglyphics 3) true 4) aluminum 5) false 6) sodium chloride 7) because the metal conducts heat away from the body faster 8) Midas 9) false 10) graphite.

Page 76. **'Pest'ological, Isn't It**: 10, 5, 4, 7, 9, 8, 3, 11, 2, 6, 12, 1.

JUNE

Page 78, **In Father's Footsteps**: 1) Leif Ericson, son of Eric the Red 2) Solomon, son of David 3) John Quincy Adams, son of John Adams 4) Johann Strauss, Jr., son of Johann Strauss, Sr. 5) Alexandre Dumas (Dumas fils), son of Alexandre Dumas (Dumas père). 6) William Pitt, son of William Pitt, Earl of Chatham 7) Henry Ward Beecher, son of Lyman Beecher 8) Oliver Wendell Holmes, son of Oliver Wendell Holmes 9) Robert Edward Lee, son of Henry Lee 10) William Booth, son of Ballington Booth.

Page 79, **Competitive Word Games for All**: The Short Word Wins: 1) aSYlum 2) sTAr 3) miSDo 4) haWSe 5) tINt 6) sTIr 7) fisH-Hook 8) sITe 9) sNIp 10) anSWer 11) miDSt 12) rATe. The Long Word Wins: 1) hikers 2) tithes 3) weather 4) tinted 5) throned 6)

breath 7) internes 8) mention 9) intonates 10) receipted 11) teatasters 12) tallower. **Let's Build a House**: Veneer, Cement, Enamel, Paint, Slate, Stone, Iron, Wood, Timber, Putty, Pipe, Plaster, Plane, Beam, Solder, Dowel, Clay, Tile, Lumber, Lead, Wire, Steel, Nails, Rivet, Concrete.

Pages 80–81, **Can You Rhyme These Celebrities**: 1a Edison 1b Madison; 2a Machiavelli 2b Botticelli; 3a Grant 3b Kant; 4a Wren 4b Penn; 5a Lafayette 5b Marquette; 6a Hippocrates 6b Socrates; 7a Poe 7b Low; 8a Cellini 8b Bellini; 9a Blake 9b Drake; 10a Key 10b Lee; 11a Handel 11b Mendel; 12a Bell 12b Tell; 13a Tasso 13b Picasso; 14a Galton 14b Dalton; 15a Snead 15b Reed; 16a Mailer 16b Taylor; 17a Paine 17b Twain; 18a Whitehead 18b Bankhead; 19a Nixon 19b Vixen; 20a Churchill 20b Hill. **Can You Beat the Songwriter**: 1a Moon 1b June; 2a Balloon 2b Tribune; 3a Impugn 3b Picaroon; 4a Inopportune 4b Baboon; 5a Immune 5b Raccoon; 6a Boon 6b Jejune; 7a Importune 7b Typhoon; 8a Prune 8b Poltroon; 9a Attune 9b Tycoon; 10a Maroon 10b Neptune.

Page 82, **Can You Pass the Buck Logically**: 4-2-8-6-3-5-1-7.

Page 83, **How Quick-Witted Are You**: 1) Expert Explanation: Undetected murders of any kind can hardly be the basis for statistics. 2) Division is Vexation: Turn it upside down and you will be able to divide it by 9. 3) Are You Sister-and-Brotherwise: 4 brothers, 3 sisters. 4) Untimely Homecoming: When he saw that his watch had stopped at 12:30, he started it going again. The next day he had to note only the difference shown on his watch and the correct time and then to figure out what time 12:30 would represent. **Sleight of Mind**: From top to bottom: King of spades, ace of hearts, ace of diamonds, king of hearts. **Shell Game Variety**: Nine of diamonds, jack of clubs, two of spades. **Chief or Thief**: 1) Thief (A pirate) 2) Chief (Leading dancer) 3) Chief (Guide for soldiers) 4) Chief (Indian chief) 5) Thief (Embezzler) 6) Chief (Business leader) 7) Chief (Indian chief) 8) Thief (Pirate) 9) Chief (East Indian chief) 10) Chief (Turkish commander) 11) Thief (Pirate) 12) Thief (Burmese) 13) Thief (Literary thief) 14) Thief (Freebooter)

Page 84, **How's Your Guesswork**: 1) Everybody (and some) would know about the murder at 2 P.M. on the same day, 5,230,-176,600 people exactly. 2) A surefire investment: Let us suppose that the "hairiest" human being has 1 million hairs on his head —which is much more than scientists say there are on anyone's head. Now here is the proof that there must be at least two people with the same number of hairs on their heads: Person #1 may have 1 hair, person #2 may have 2 hairs, #3 three hairs, and so forth up to person #1,000,000 who would have 1 million hairs. But as there are about 3 billion people living on earth, the million and first person *must necessarily* have a number of hairs lying between 1 hair and 1 million hairs, i.e. the same number of hairs someone else has. 3) April 29, 1902, at 10:40 P.M. 4) Four colors only. This is based on experience, as no mathematical proof for this accepted fact has been put forward as yet. 5) 41,000 years. This time can be exactly calculated by multiplying $1 \times 2 \times 3 \times 4 \times 5$ and so forth up to 15 which results in this amazingly high number. 6) 45 pounds of dust, although dust is particularly light material and it takes many billions of particles to make up one ounce. 7) In 128 different ways. 8) Many people will answer 20, 30, 40, etc. pounds. Some cautious ones might estimate the weight of the sphere at several hundred pounds. Actually, such a sphere would weight about 20,000 pounds. 9) The panhandler will get only a little less than $4,000, strange as it may seem. Even if he would see the nabob every day of his life he would never get an exact $40.00 but always a little less. 10) At the age of 55, the man would certainly have paid the 2 billion tab, as his heart would have beaten more than 2 billion times by that time.

Page 85, **Riddles, Riddles, Riddles**: 1) Because he was a stickup man. 2) Make sure one of them is a match. 3) "Thanks very much. I'll never part with it." 4) Letters. 5) One is a hobgoblin and the other is a gob hobblin'. 6) The elevator, the alarm clock, and the ladder. 7) Noise. 8) You always find them in beds. 9) A map. 10) Because it has no point. 11) Shredded tweet. 12) A ferris wheel. 13) Because both of them go on a line. 14) Automobile. 15) Close the door between you. 16) His fingernail.

Page 86, **How 'Mirror'able Are You**: Solution: I) Third house; store window and sign. Fourth house; chimney and door, center strip. Fifth house; three top windows, grocery window. Eighth house; window, bottom panel. 11) 1) nails in helmet 2) glove 3) tail 4) tail cover 5) saddle 6) plume 7) knee plate 8) spur.

Page 87, **What Goes On in the Letter Circle**: For Youngsters: A) MITE B) MAYO C) YEA D) EATS E) YOSEMITE F) CALM G) TOP H) ELGAR I) ANNOY J) STOP K) SCHUMANN L) SEMI M) MAY N) YEATS O) ALMA P) RUB Q) BEN R) HUMAN S) RUBE T) CHUM U) EAT V) CAL W) HUM X) MAN Y) EMIT Z) PAS. For Parents: A) SEMITE B) RUBENS C) MITE D) MAYO E) HUMAN F) RUBE G) YEATS H) ALMA I) GAR J) ELGAR K) HUM L) MANN M) SCHUMANN N) BEN O) CALM P) CHUM Q) RUB R) YOSEMITE S) MAY T) PASCAL U) TOP V) EMIT W) STOP X) ANNOY Y) MAN Z) PAS.

Pages 88–89, **Family Quiz Game**: WOMEN: (1) a (2) true (3) Switzerland (4) House of Commons (5) Franz Liszt (6) Capulet (7) Louisa May Alcott (8) true (Anna Freud) (9) Eugene O'Neill (10) Victoria Woodhull, 1872. MURDER: (1) Lincoln, Garfield, McKinley, Kennedy (2) Banquo (3) Julius Caesar (4) McKinley (5) true (Earl Warren) (6) Charles J. Guiteau (7) Sarajevo (8) Francis Ferdinand, Archduke of Austria (9) José (10) Murder must be intentional. NUMBERS & TIME: (1) 1:30 (2) 2 dimes, 5 pennies (3) four (4) five (5) dozen (6) four (7) eight (8) two years (9) twelve (10) sixty. MAMMALS: (1) None—they eat only vegetables (2) opossum (3) ram (4) true (5) filly (6) gorilla (7) pig (8) true (9) c (10) African. BRITAIN: (1) the "Union Jack" (2) rugby (3) anglophile (4) France (5) George III (6) 10 Downing Street (7) after (1833) (8) Shetland (9) true (10) King Arthur. SPORTS: (1) Norway (2) bowling (3) true (4) home base (5) "Anchors Aweigh" (6) Abner Doubleday (7) Shea Stadium (8) b (9) Candlestick Park (10) caddie.

Page 90. **Can You Couple These Couples**: 1-Spain-O(1); 2-Japan-N; 3-Austria-E; 4-Ethiopia-W; 5-India-O(2); 6-Russia-R; 7-Scotland-L; 8-Modern-D. Anagram: One World.

JULY

Page 92, **Thomas, No Doubt**: 1) Thomas Jefferson 2) Thomas Gainsborough 3) Tommy Tucker 4) Thomas Edison 5) Thomas Mann 6) Thomas More 7) Tommy Atkins 8) Thomas Hobbes 9) Thomas Paine 10) Thomas Dewey 11) Thomas Hardy 12) Thomas Carlyle 13) Thomas Hart Benton. **Red, White or Blue**: YOUNGSTERS: 1) Red 2) Red 3) Red 4) Red 5) Red 6) Red 7) Red 8) Red 9) Blue 10) Red 11) White 12) Blue 13) White 14) Blue 15) Red 16) Blue

17) Red 18) Red 19) Red 20) Red 21) Red 22) Blue 23) White 24) Red. PARENTS: 1) Red (like the stone) 2) White (like gypsum) 3) Blue (like seawater) 4) White (like silver) 5) Blue (like sky) 6) Red (like the flower) 7) Blue (like azurite) 8) Red (like cardinal's hat) 9) Blue (like sky) 10) Red (like wine) 11) Blue (like sky) 12) Red (like rose) 13) Blue (like dye) 14) Red (pigment from lac) 15) Red (like fuchsine) 16) Red (like Tuscan red) 17) Red (like mulberry) 18) Red (like blood) 19) Blue (like the stone) 20) Red (like Venetian red) 21) Red (like fuchsine) 22) Red (like Titian's favorite color) 23) Blue (like the stone) 24) Blue (like lapis lazuli).

Page 93, **Competitive Word Games for All**: The Short Word Wins: 1) eiGHt 2) aLTo 3) pORe 4) dRUm 5) lIOn 6) dOFf 7) dUSt 8) isSUe 9) aFOot 10) bOIl 11) pURe 12) fROm 13) aTLas 14) fisHGing. The Long Word Wins: 1) manger 2) verily 3) locust 4) target 5) derails 6) mention 7) enduring 8) severing 9) therefor 10) cannoned 11) marinate 12) boarder 13) protean 14) habitation. **How's Your Perspective Perspicacity**: 1) Girl's hat on bench 2) Clothes rack 3) Door seen from above 4) Candle in candlestick 5) Suitcase 6) Iron 7) Hammer.

Page 94, **Odd Ones Out**: 1b) not ending in 'ave' 2c) not reading the same backward 3c) meaning move without using a man-made vehicle 4d) not an anagram of mister 5d) not starting with a bird's name 6d) meaning a 'solid' among planes 7d) meaning an organ not connected with the senses 8c) not ending in a number 9c) without two consecutive doublets 10a) denoting a definite period of time 11c) not also the name of a plant 12e) not ending with its initial letter 13d) not also a Roman numeral 14a) for a city not also the word for a headgear 15a) not meaning pertaining to a certain planet 16d) not containing all vowels just once 17d) containing the idea of ONE instead of TWO 18a) that is indefinite, the others mean finished art works 19e) that cannot be anagrammed into an animal's name as APE, EWE, BAT, RAM 20c) not resulting in another word when read backward 21a) not also the word for a ship of some kind 22d) not ending in the name of a fish 23d) not ending in some pronoun 24c) pronounced differently from the others 25b) not containing a tree within. **A Buttony Problem**: The circles are all the SAME size.

Page 95, **Do You Know the Long and the Short of It**: 1) False 2) True 3) True 4) False 5) True 6) False 7) False 8) True 9) True 10)

True. **Hidden Words**: S + Leaf + Bird − F − Bear + Rose − Dress + N = LION.

Pages 96–97, **No answers needed**.

Page 98, **To Each His Horse**: 1–Indian's horse-A: 2–Indian elephant-N; 3–Bolivian llama–O(1); 4–Race horse–T; 5–Arabian dromedary–H; 6–Knight's steed–E; 7–Witch's broom–R(1); 8–Trojan horse–C; 9–Cowboy's horse–O(2); 10–Rocking horse–L; 11–Vaulting horse–O(3); 12–Circus horse–R (2). Anagram: Another Color.

Page 99, **How Quick-Witted Are You**: 1) A Fine Problem: No fine at all. The man was only daydreaming. 2) A Touching Problem A = 3, B = 4, C = 6, D = 5, E = 4. 3) Odd Encounter: Only one of them was born in the U.S. Hence, if both meet in the U.S., the pal born here has entered the U.S. as many times as he left it while the other must have entered it once more. 4) Double, Double, Toil and Treble:

```
2 1 9
4 3 8
6 5 7

3 2 7
6 5 4
9 8 1
```

5) Silence for Four Minutes: Two to two to two too.

Page 100. **Five at One Stroke**:

The Number Game:

$72 \times 13 = 936$			$525 \div 7 = 75$		
+	−	−		− + +
$774 \div 9 = 86$			$110 \times 3 = 330$		
$846 + 4 = 850$			$415 − 10 = 405$		

Page 101. **What Goes On in the Letter Circle**: For Youngsters: A) GASH B) FORD C) GNAT D) SHOWER E) HAWAII F) KERN G) BERTH H) ROB I) SHAW J) ERNE K) GAS L) HOWE M) SHOW N) HAW O) ASH P) ROBERT Q) HOW R) OWER S) ELF T) HOOK U) FOR V) ROBE W) OK X) KERNEL Y) IGNATIUS Z) US. For Parents: A) HOOK B) IGNATIUS C) ASH D) HAW E) HAWAII F) KERNEL G) DEGAS H) ERNE I) FORD J) SHOWER K) GNAT L) HOWE M) GASH N) HOOKER O) BERTH P) SHAW Q) ROB R) HOW S) ROBERT T) KERN

U) OWE V) ROBE W) SHOW X) FOR Y) ASH Z) WE US.

Pages 102–103, **Family Quiz Game**: POETRY: (1) T.S. Eliot (2) couplet (3) Emily Dickinson (4) Swinburne (5) true (6) Tennyson (7) Clement C. Moore (8) tone poem (9) John Keats (10) Carl Sandburg. GOVERNMENT: (1) William Fulbright (2) with the concurrence of two-thirds (3) the Vice President (4) the Senate (5) five (6) Harry Truman's (7) the President's signature, or passage by Congress over his veto (8) voters of the entire state (9) the mace (10) on the first Monday after the second Wednesday in December. GEOGRAPHY: (1) Italy (2) California (3) Washington, D.C. (4) false (5) continent (6) heavy (7) b (8) b (9) Alaska (10) West. PLANES & FIGURES: (1) five million (2) three (3) two (4) thirty-six (5) eight (6) 100 (7) twelve (8) two triangles (9) XXXIII (10) six. NATURAL HISTORY: 1) cocoon (2) spruce (3) raccoon (4) on the ocean floor (5) b (6) The date fruit grows on the date palm tree (7) true (8) no (9) avocado (10) the arctic tern (it nests in the Arctic and spends the winter in the Antarctic. FIRST AND LAST: (1) Betsy Ross (2) Delaware (3) Hawaii (4) Delaware (5) Boston, Mass. (6) Moon, Earth, Sun (7) Tokyo (8) Genesis (9) Fourscore (10) Explorer.

Page 104, **The Most Ridiculous Game Ever Played**: 1) Both teams have not changed ends after half time. 2) The building in the rear has one more story (time too short to complete entire story). 3) The soccer ball (round) has been exchanged for a football (oval). 4) The goalkeeper has lost his mustache in second picture. 5) The scoreboard shows more goals scored in the first half than in the second. 6) The umpire has white hair in the second picture. 7) The clock has stayed at the same hour. 8) The goalie has a black cap with a white stripe in the second picture.

AUGUST

Page 106, **Voyages to Nowhere**: 1) Atlantis 2) Estotiland 3) Utopia 4) Eden 5) Cockaigne 6) Lilliput 7) Brobdingnag 8) Isles of the Hesperides 9) El Dorado 10) Valhalla 11) Seventh Heaven (Islam) 12) Elysium.

Page 107, **Competitive Word Games for All**: The Short Word Wins: 1) etHYl 2) krAAl 3) uPDo 4) sPIt 5) stYLe 6) sHOp 7) nOHow 8) sLYly 9) rIPe 10) deaDPan 11) bazAAr 12) boYHood. The Long Word Wins: 1) moans 2) ranted 3) repine 4) pencil 5) dilute 6) choirs 7) bitters 8) trailer 9) vindicate 10) mounted 11) rationales 12) tethering. **Eye Spy**: Faces 7 and 10

Page 108, **Can You Get the Writers Right**: 1o, 2i, 3h, 4f, 5c, 6n, 7m, 8l, 9k, 10b, 11a, 12e, 13d 14g 15j.

Page 109, **To Quote or to Misquote**: 1) learning 2) sufficient 3) woods 4) powder 5) most 6) kindness 7) is 8) reckoning 9) better 10) merry 11) no 12) falls 13) mirth 14) nor any 15) glisters 16) joins 17) on 18) before 19) more richer 20) Englishman.

Page 110, **Dream Shop of the Future—300 Years Ago**: 1) map of the United States 2) price tag (dollars) 3) spool of thread 4) light bulb 5) Eiffel Tower model 6) sewing machine 7) telephone 8) statue of Napoleon 9) top hat 10) book by Victor Hugo 11) pencil behind ear of shopkeeper 12) cigarette in hand of shopkeeper 13) pocket watch 14) train 15) alarm clock 16) ice cream soda. **Trees in the Letter Forest**: Holly, Cedar, Elder, Cherry, Pear, Pine, Ash, Poplar, Larch, Elm, Alder, Plum, Lime, Aspen, Medlar, Lilac.

Page 111, **Riddles, Riddles, Riddles**: 1) Because it follows a regular beat. 2) Safe robbery. 3) If you give them an inch, they'll take a yard. 4) A pavement. 5) An umbrella. 6) A wedding ring. 7) Because that is where their funnybones are. 8) From a hen. 9) Smiles; there is a mile between the first letter and the last. 10) If you don't see sharp, you'll be flat. 11) Two-um plus two-um. 12) "I'm stumped!" 13) The preserved pairs. 14) A circle. 15) Answer-ring. 16) Because he is always selling that which he kneads himself. 17) The smallest. 18) A blind horse. 19) Jump! 20) It just shuts up and says nothing. 21) An egg. 22) A fountain.

Page 112, **The Great Memory Quiz**: 1) Yes–soda glass 2) Yes–bathtub 3) No–record only, no player 4) Yes–piggybank 5) No 6) No 7) Yes–pen 8) Yes–fork 9) No 10) Yes–compass 11) No–easel only, no paint 12) Yes–camera 13) Yes–shoe 14) No 15) Yes–gimlet 16) Yes–screw 17) No 18) No 19) Yes–bulb 20) No 21) Yes–comb 22) Yes–clock 23) Yes–anchor 24) Yes–coffeemill 25) Yes–bottle 26) Yes–corkscrew 27) Yes–hypodermic 28) No 29) Yes–specs 30) Yes–opera glasses 31) Yes–hammer 32) Yes–knife 33) No 34) Yes–parachute 35) No–only one card 36) No 37) Yes–triangle 38) Yes–atomizer 39) Yes–spade 40) Yes–teacup.

Pages 114–115, **Family Quiz Game**: MUSIC: (1) a 64th note (2) Fritz Kreisler, Yehudi Menuhin, Jascha Heifetz (3) c (4) Claude Debussy (5) strings, woodwinds, brass, percussion (6) pianoforte (7) John Philip Sousa (8) concerto (9) Frank Loesser (10) coda. U.S. HISTORY: (1) Henry Clay

184

(2) Jefferson's (3) Andrew Jackson (4) the Federalists and the Democratic-Republican Party (5) 1866 (6) the 13th (7) Peter Minuit (8) Norman Thomas (9) Woodrow Wilson (10) Eisenhower (Denison, Texas), Truman (Lamar, Mo.), Hoover (West Branch, Ia.) THE BODY: (1) cavity (2) two (3) two (4) true (5) twenty-one (6) pinkie (7) neck (8) the nose (9) legs (10) palm. SHIPS: (1) no–very strong oak (2) a rope (3) tugboat (4) Mayflower (5) c (6) submarine (7) Noah (8) true (9) sailboat (10) Admiral Farragut. AUTHORS: (1) Hans Christian Andersen (2) Mark Twain (Samuel Clemens) (3) Stephen Foster (4) Abraham Lincoln (5) true (6) Edgar Rice Burroughs (7) John Lennon of the Beatles (8) "Poor Richard's Almanack" (9) James Fenimore Cooper (10) Thomas Jefferson. MORE OR LESS: (1) the Old (2) both are of the same weight: 1 pound (3) a three-foot square contains 9 square feet (4) hydrogen (5) the Suez (6) acute (7) the pound (about $2.40) (8) true (9) larger (10) more.

Page 116, **What Goes On in the Letter Circle**: For Youngsters: A) SONS B) HELL C) TENNYSON D) ART E) WALT F) YEW G) MOBILE H) MOB I) WISE J) CHART K) LEWIS L) MO M) CHAR N) HARTE O) ALTO P) SHELL Q) ALAMO R) TON S) SEA T) EYE U) SHELLEY V) TENN W) ALA X) BILE Y) WIS Z) ILE For Parents: A) HELL B) SHELLEY C) TONAL D) WALTON E) BILE F) TENNYSON G) EACH H) TEN I) ALAMO J) LEWIS K) ELL L) WISE M) ALTONA N) MOB O) MOBILE P) SEA Q) ART R) HARTE S) LAM T) ACH U) OBI) V) YEW W) ELLE X) ALTON Y) TON Z) HART.

SEPTEMBER

Page 118, **How Soundwise Are You**: YOUNGSTERS: 1) bare 2) stake 3) sun 4) tense 5) leak 6) hair 7) peek 8) dye 9) two 10) pear 11) lye 12) feet 13) mane 14) fair 15) soar. PARENTS: 1) minor 2) hoarse 3) altar 4) plumb 5) pane 6) knight 7) hie 8) hoard 9) forth 10) raze 11) aye 12) feint 13) martial 14) heir 15) canon 16) caste 17) augur 18) beau 19) route 20) plait 21) urn 22) dough 23) rhyme 24) dun 25) soccer 26) clime 27) colonel 28) fête 29) quire 30) palette 31) divisor 32) cruise 33) wreak 34) sine 35) baron 36) ruff. DIFFICULT: 37a) rein b) reign 38a) gnu b) knew 39a) bel b) belle 40a) right b) wright 41a) frieze b) freeze 42a) meat b) mete 43a) sight b) cite 44a) vane b) vein 45a) idol b) idyl 46a) ewe b) yew.

Page 119, **Competitive Word Games for**

All: The Short Word Wins: 1) fisHSkin 2) mANe 3) cROw 4) aVOw 5) hEMp 6) paSTe 7) iTSelf 8) aMEn 9) rOVe 10) sORe 11) sNAp 12) aSHy. The Long Word Wins: 1) hurled 2) remain 3) miracle 4) credit 5) leather 6) tobies 7) thither 8) stammers 9) trooped 10) libation 11) lightning 12) gauntlets. **A Grave Error**: If Mary died before her husband, how could she be his widow?

Page 120, **Geography: True, False, or Both**: 1) a-c 2) a-b 3) b 4) a 5) b 6) b 7) b 8) c 9) a 10) c 11) a 12) b

Page 121, **'State'ly Expressions**: 1) f 2) i 3) g 4) h 5) o 6) k 7) m 8) j 9) n 10) a 11) d 12) b 13) e 14) c 15) l. **Cosmopolitan Cooking**: 1) Russia 2) France 3) USA 4) Italy 5) Hungary 6) Germany 7) Mexico 8) India 9) Poland 10) England 11) Austria 12) Turkey 13) Spain 14) Switzerland 15) Arabia 16) Czechoslovakia.

Pages 122–123, **No answers needed.**

Page 124, **A Tempestuous Problem**: 1) Medieval Lady I(1); 2) Businessman T; 3) Gypsy S; 4) Cook A; 5) Witch N(1); 6) Indian I(2); 7) Diver L(1); 8) Child L(2); 9) Queen W; 10) Cowboy I (3); 11) Roman Gladiator N(2); 12) Jester D—Anagram: IT'S AN ILL WIND.

Page 125, **Country Idyl Slightly Wacky**: 1) bananas in tree 2) bird upside down in nest 3) apples in maple tree 4) swing ends on the horizon, not in tree 5) duck has wrong feet 6) rabbit has wrong tail 7) pail has hole in bottom but still holds water 8) penguin 9) rooster on hen's nest 10) fish in nest 11) boy on fence has different pants legs 12) flag on house blowing in one direction—smoke in another. **Be A Match-Magician**:

Page 126, **Who Missed the Ark**: NOAH: Lion – Kangaroo – Zebra – Ostrich.

Page 127, **What Goes On in the Letter Circle**: For Youngsters: A) RYE B) TAFT C) CHOW D) BOAR E) COOPER F) HOW G) OAR H) YET I) HALE J) RICH K) BRIG L) SCOOP M) ALE N) PERRY O) ETA P) RIG Q) OWE R) ERIC S) BOA T) BRIGADE U) HALER V) COOP W) WEB X) DEB Y) ERR Z) AD For Parents: A) GAD B) TAFT C) DEB D) PERRY E) RYE F) HALE G) WEB H) BRIGADE I) ICH J) BALBOA K) SCOOP L) ALB M)

COOPER N) BOAR O) HOWE P) ALE Q) ADE R) BRIG S) THALER T) RICH U) BOA V) ARTS W) RIGA X) CHOW Y) BALBO Z) COO.

Pages 128–129, **Family Quiz Game**: FOOD: (1) a. pear b. peach c. apple (2) epicure (3) b (4) blackberry and red raspberry (5) Japan (6) cabbage (the only one that grows above the ground) (7) the Indians of the New World (8) Thomas Wolfe (9) cheese (10) bouillabaisse. STAGE: (1) Arthur Miller (2) *Oedipus Rex* (3) Macbeth (4) Verdi (5) Raymond Massey (6) Rossini's *Barber of Seville* and Mozart's *Marriage of Figaro* (7) Lorenz Hart (8) Globe (9) Eugene O'Neill (10) John Barrymore. UNITED STATES: (1) skyscrapers (2) 1492 (3) White House (4) New York City (5) the Pilgrims (6) money (7) George Washington (8) papoose (9) four (10) Vice-President. STORYBOOK CHARACTERS: (1) the small one (2) the rabbit (3) Emerald City (4) Christopher Robin (5) Captain Hook (6) Mowgli (7) the spindle of a spinning wheel (8) James Bond (9) Lilliputians (10) miser. SPACE: (1) Gemini rockets (2) c (3) seven (4) Polaris (5) nine (6) length, width, depth (7) Mars (8) Saturn (9) Sun (10) Mt. Palomar, Cal. DISCOVERERS: (1) Kublai Khan (2) before (3) Ponce de León (4) Vasco Núñez de Balboa (5) Hernando de Soto (6) Wilhelm Roentgen (7) Marie Curie (8) Robert Peary (9) Roald Amundsen (10) Peru.

Page 130, **Odd Objects Out**: COLUMN A: peas not a fruit; scorpion not an insect; clock has no poles; thimble not a barber's tool; watering can not a kitchen utensil; collar has no knot. COLUMN B: knife not used for cleaning; camera produces pictures; candle not used for smoking; pistol only firearm; accordion is wind instrument not played with the mouth; boomerang only weapon. COLUMN C: saddle not cowboy wearing apparel; moon shines by reflected light; bat only mammal; ace no face card; fox no rodent; gimlet not a smith's tool.

OCTOBER

Page 132, **Do You Know Your Spirits**: 1c, 2e, 3i, 4h, 5o, 6n, 7k, 8l, 9b, 10j, 11f, 12g, 13a, 14d, 15m.

Page 133, **Competitive Word Games for All**: The Short Word Wins: 1) sCYthe 2) bOAr 3) goLDy 4) rUSe 5) sMUg 6) aBBey 7) nUMb 8) uSUrp 9) iDLe 10) gAOl. The Long Word Wins: 1) balmy 2) choir 3) unreel 4) nuclear 5) remains 6) brave 7) sprout 8) snouters 9) indicated 10) orations. **Hidden Words**: Car + Pen + Owl − Pear − N +

Sun + A − Swan + M + Brush − Rh = COLUMBUS

Page 134, **International Double-Talk—In Plain English**: 1) French 2) Russian 3) Greek 4) Japanese 5) Peruvian 6) Dutch 7) Hungarian 8) Persian 9) German 10) Polish 11) English 12) Turkish 13) Belgian 14) Norwegian 15) Danish 16) Italian 17) Chinese 18) Portuguese 19) Australian 20) Irish 21) Roman 22) Spanish 23) Egyptian 24) Swedish 25) Swiss 26) Brazilian 27) Chilean.

Page 135, **How Sharp Are You at Sign Language**: 1) Repeat − Space 2) Scruple − Moon − Earth 3) Bar − Male − Female 4) Take − Positive − Is greater 5) Ounce 6) Difference 7) Opposition − Mix 8) Root − Yen − Square 9) Degree − Natural 10) Sum − Turn.

Page 136, **Odd Dish Out**: 1) Cream puffs: Small cakes in the group of appetizers. 2) Petits fours: Small cakes in the group of breads. 3) Julep: A kind of brandy or whisky in the group of beers. 4) Biscuit tortoni: An ice cream in the group of soups. 5) Kumquat: A fruit in the group of vegetables. 6) Charlotte russe: A gelatin pudding in the group of potatoes. 7) Mock crab: A cheese dish in the group of seafood. 8) Turkey: Poultry in the group of game. 9) Spare ribs: Pork in the group of beef. 10) Partridge: Game in the group of poultry. 11) Marron glacé: A candy in the group of ices. 12) Yorkshire pudding: A meat dish in the group of sweet puddings. 13) Timbale: A meat or fish dish in the group of cheese dishes. 14) Moselle: A white wine in the group of red wines. 15) Cognac: A brandy in the group of liqueurs.

Page 137, **From Soup to Nuts and Beyond**: 1) port 2) sardines 3) pea soup 4) duck soup 5) fish 6) ham 7) beef 8) stew 9) rolls 10) crackers 11) eggs 12) squash 13) corn 14) mushrooms 15) relish 16) tea 17) cake 18) applesauce 19) nuts 20) ices. **A Hungry Man**:

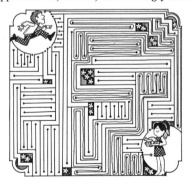

Page 138, **The Problem of the Wiry Men**: MUCH DRIVE. **Riddles, Riddles, Riddles**: 1) Their hair grows out in bangs. 2) The letter B. 3) A goat. 4) It wasn't raining. 5) Nine cents. 6) A kitten. 7) Your teeth. 8) When we double our fists. 9) Because he thought he would get a kick out of it. 10) Because it had a windowpane. 11) A needle. 12) Your word. 13) A coat of paint. 14) Because you can always hear a pin drop. 15) An umbrella. 16) A box of quackers. 17) When the door is open. 18) Tulips. 19) Because it has rocks in its bed. 20) Telling a hair-raising story to a baldheaded man. 21) Sixteen – 4 better, 4 worse, 4 richer, 4 poorer.

Page 139, **Shapes in Nature**: A-4 South America; B-6 Armadillo; C-2 Crab; D-5 Spider; B-1 Mountain; F-3 Guinea Fowl.

Page 140, **Actors Anonymous**: 1a) Don Quixote 2n) Cyrano de Bergerac 3j) Dante Alighieri 4c) Christopher Columbus 5d) Sherlock Holmes 6e) Napoleon 7i) Adolf Hitler 8b) Diogenes 9k) Hamlet 10h) Nero 11l)Paris 12f) Robin Hood 13g)William Tell 14m) Caesar

Page 141, **What Goes On in the Letter Circle**: For Youngsters: A) LOG B) HAYES C) DIN D) O'NEILL E) AYES F) YES G) ARTHUR H) ILL I) DO J) HURL K) AHA L) HIVE M) NOAH N) AND O) GANDHI P) HAY Q) DON R) VERDI S) ART T) RAH U) LIND V) DONE W) SARAH X) THUR Y) HUR Z) ONE. For Parents: A) HAY B) GANDHI C) YES D) RAH E) AHA F) SARAH G) DINO H) NOAH I) HIVER J) AYES K) LIND L) LOGAN M) HART N) DONE O) VERDI P) DON Q) LOG R) ARTHUR S) O'NEILL T) HURL U) ONE V) HAYES W) ILL X) HUR Y) LIN Z) ARA.

Pages 142–143, **Family Quiz Game**: WARDROBE: (1) Mother Hubbard (2) Angora goat (3) true (4) obi (5) Rudi Gernreich (6) haute couture (7) light tan or light beige (8) a type of shoes (9) from the blouse worn by midshipmen (10) cowl. SCIENCE: (1) Fe (2) catalyst (3) pacemaker (4) hemoglobin (5) amount of electric current (6) yes (7) entomology (8) seismograph (9) Norbert Wiener (10) Skinner box. FAIRY TALES: (1) true (2) swan (3) *Snow White and the Seven Dwarfs* (4) a pumpkin (5) Mr. MacGregor's (6) Androcles (7) Rose Red (8) the Tin Woodman (9) the dormouse (10) tortoise. SPORTS & GAMES: (1) polo (2) baseball (3) bull's-eye (4) true (5) eleven (6) zero (7) baseball (8) a lefthander (9) b. (10) horsehide. PRESIDENTS: (1) Thomas Jefferson (2) Twentieth (3) Lincoln's Gettysburg Ad-

dress (4) Mount Vernon (5) Kentucky (6) false (7) John Wilkes Booth (8) Eisenhower (9) James Monroe (10) false (he was Senator). ANATOMY: (1) the upper and lower chambers of the heart (2) c (3) true (4) c (5) c (6) b (7) cytology (8) involuntary (9) to listen to heart action (10) a.

Page 144, **State Those States**: 1) Maine–ME., 2) Washington–WASH., 3) Pennsylvania–PA., 4) Maryland–MD., 5) Kansas–KAN. (can), 6) Alabama–ALA., 7) Oregon–ORE., 8) Ohio–O., 9) Idaho–ID., 10) Louisiana–LA., 11) Massachusetts–MASS., 12) Mississippi–MISS. **Palmary Logic**: 1-6-3-8-5-4-2-7.

NOVEMBER

Page 146, **Is It 'President'ially Possible**: 1) POSSIBLE–Washington served in the English army against the French. 2) IMPOSSIBLE–The amendment to forbid third terms was ratified in 1951. 3) IMPOSSIBLE–The 100th birthday of Adams would have been in 1837 while postage stamps were not authorized till 1847. 4) IMPOSSIBLE–The charter was never formally signed. 5) POSSIBLE–The letter was written. 6) POSSIBLE–John Adams and Thomas Jefferson both died on July 4, 1826. 7) IMPOSSIBLE–Daguerre did not perfect the process of obtaining images on a plate of silver till 1839; Lincoln was postmaster till 1836. 8) POSSIBLE–John Quincy Adams was president when his father John Adams was alive. 9) POSSIBLE–He was at one time Police Commissioner of New York City. 10) POSSIBLE–A historic fact. 11) POSSIBLE–McKinley was killed by two pistol shots. 12) IMPOSSIBLE–There are no tigers in Africa. 13) IMPOSSIBLE–Baseball did not become an organized game till much later. 14) IMPOSSIBLE–Japan had been isolated from the Western world until Commodore Perry's first visit there in 1854—4 years after Taylor's term. 15) POSSIBLE–Garfield was very much interested in carpentry. 16) POSSIBLE–This item is in the Historical Museum of Tennessee. 17) IMPOSSIBLE–The Monroe Doctrine was a message to Congress but never ratified. 18) IMPOSSIBLE–Buchanan never married. 19)IMPOSSIBLE–The U.S. was never a member of the League. 20) IMPOSSIBLE–Cleveland, long in existence before, was named after Moses Cleveland.

Page 147, **Competitive Word Games for All**: The Short Word Wins: 1) enVYing 2) dEAl 3) ouTDo 4) rESt 5) eRNe 6) krAAl 7) eNRol 8) uSEd 9) reDTop 10) pAEan. The

Long Word Wins: 1) rivet 2) image 3) deport 4) pestle 5) crochet 6) tarragon 7) leaving 8) replicas 9) creative 10) colorist. **Low Bridge, High I.Q**: He let some air out of his tires, drove through the underpass to the service station on the other side and filled his tires again.

Page 148, **Can You Pair Them for the Ark**: 1e) Oxen, 2q) Bears, 3t) Anteaters, 4i) Monkeys, 5d) Cats, 6p) Llamas, 7m) Apes, 8s) Antelopes, 9o) Asses, 10g) Rabbits, 11f) Whales, 12b) Horses, 13r) Wolves, 14h) Ducks, 15c) Dogs, 16n) Sheep, 17j) Eels, 18a) Geese, 19k) Mountain lions, 20l) Deer. **Signs and Symbols**: 1) Architect 2) Printer 3) Mapmaker 4) Carpenter 5) Electrician 6) Accountant 7) Druggist 8) Musician 9) Astrologer 10) Banker.

Page 149, **Cow or Horse**: 1a) Cow 1b) Horse; 2a) Cow 2b) Horse; 3a) Cow 3b) Horse; 4a) Horse 4b) Cow; 5a) Horse 5b) Cow; 6a) Cow 6b) Horse; 7a) Cow 7b) Horse; 8a) Horse 8b) Cow; 9a) Horse 9b) Cow; 10a) Horse 10b) Cow; 11a) Cow 11b) Horse; 12a) Cow 12b) Horse; 13a) Cow 13b) Horse; 14a) Horse 14b) Cow; 15a) Cow 15b) Horse.

Pages 150–151, **How Practical Are You**: 1) Position B is the easier one. Position A would put an undue strain on the small of the back, especially when pressure would be required in handling the cleaner. Force should emanate from the arms, not from the whole body. 2) B is the correct answer. The small cog inside the big cog must necessarily turn in a direction opposite to that of the big cog. This small inside cog is on the same axle as Cog B, which, therefore, also turns in a direction opposite to the big cog. (A, on the other hand, will then turn in the same direction again as the big cog.) 3) B is the correct answer. To cut metal, a concentrated force is required. The construction of Shears B is such as to make best use of such concentrated force. Also, the blades are much sturdier, and their cutting angle is especially designed for the purpose. 4) B is the correct answer. The strain on Chain A would be a much greater one than the strain on Chain B if either chain were not supported by the other. It is obvious that it is easier to hold, say, a long metal bar by grasping its center than by grasping either end. 5) Vase A will tip over more easily. The center of gravity of Vase B is somewhere close to the actual center of the illustration, where it should be to assure good balance. The center of gravity of Vase A is located too high in the upper

part, so that this vase will topple more easily. 6) Since both scales balance perfectly, the answer is obviously that Weight A and Weight B are even. Though one object appears larger, its actual weight nevertheless is the same. 7) A is the correct answer. The finest gravel must be passed through the finest sieve first. The remainder goes through the other sieves, in the order of their fineness, with the coarsest last. 8) Room A has more of an echo than Room B. The carpet as well as the curtains and some of the furniture will absorb some of the sound in Room B, so that the echo will be more pronounced in the emptier Room A. 9) The correct answer is A. 10) The correct answer is B. This is a problem, similar to number five, involving the center of gravity, which, in Illustration A, is where it should be—in the actual center of the table—while, in Illustration B, too much weight is put on the right side of the table. Wrong leverage might thus cause damage to Table B. 11) The door marked B would be easier to open. A construction involving curved hinges might prove highly impracticable, if not actually impossible. 12) Man B has the heavier load. Again the problem is one of the center of gravity. It is easy to see that the load is to the right of center, thus making more demands on the lifting powers of Man B than on those of Man A.

Page 152, **How Quick-Witted Are You**: 1) Climbing to the Peak of Confusion: 4 boys —2 girls, in this order: Boy, Boy, Father, Girl, Girl, Mother, Boy, Boy. 2) It's Almost Impossible: Take glass #2, pour its contents into empty glass #5, and then put it back in its place. 3) Personal Get-Together: IT WILL BE: U and ME = EMU, U and HE = HUE WE and HER = WHERE. 4) Touchy Problem with Teeth: Pieces 1 and 4. 5) Elusive Lucy: Lucy is picking flowers. 6) Move a Match and Be Equal: a) $\sqrt{1} = 1$ b) $1 \times 11 = 11$ c) $1 = 1 = 1$ d) $11 - \square = 11$ 7) What's Your Score: Take it by all means, as the score before any game starts is always zero—zero.

Page 153, **The Twins' Birthday Problem**: One—Watch, Bow, Piggybank; Three—Sailboats; Four—Teddy bears.

Page 154, **Wanted: Two Men**: A = 14, B = 3, **Musical Message**: Urgent: *Ed* go to the *cafe*. Arrest Joe, the *bad* hombre. If you meet *face* to *face*, don't expect him to *beg* for mercy. Draw your gun, show your *badge*, and arrest him at once.

Page 155, **What Goes On in the Letter Circle**: For Youngsters: A) CURIE B) ROD

C) LAND D) DREW E) ANDREW F) DAD G) WILL H) SPA I) ABE J) ADAMS K) PAN L) CUR M) NAB N) BEAR O) ANDREWS P) BEARD Q) ADAM R) LUTHER S) HERO T) DIN U) DAM V) ELAND W) SWILL X) ANA Y) ILL Z) HEROD. For Parents: A) INCUR B) BEARD C) ODIN D) BEAR E) WILL F) PAN G) RODIN H) ANA I) LUTHER J) CURIE K) HERO L) SPAN M) DADA N) ANDREW O) EAR P) ELAN Q) ADAMS R) SWILL S) URIEL T) ANDREWS U) ABE V) LAND W) SPA X) URI Y) DAM Z) ELAND .

Pages 156–157, **Family Quiz Game**: WOMEN: (1) Lucie Manette (2) the Tudors (3) Joan of Arc (4) Evelyn Lincoln (5) Indira Gandhi (6) Amelia Earhart (7) Mona Lisa's (8) Vassar (9) Aunt Chloe (10) true. MYTHOLOGY: (1) Gorgon (2) Atlas (3) Pluto (4) Pandora (5) Circe (6) Excalibur (7) Janus (8) Aphrodite (9) Icarus (10) goat. NATURE: (1) in Maine (2) false (3) true (4) true (5) salt water (6) heat it (7) yes (8) animal (sheep) (9) three sides (10) true. POSERS: (1) yes (2) during the first hour or at one o'clock (3) $5 \times 8 = 40$ (4) Cardinals (5) four times (6) geese (7) one million (8) lemon (9) melon (10) aunt. WORDS: (1) suspenders (2) b (they are antonyms) (3) predicate (4) a (5) contract (6) very sociable (7) sailor (8) were (9) c (10) synonyms. WAR: (1) Jefferson Davis (2) Massachusetts (3) John Paul Jones (4) James Madison (5) Poland (6) carpetbaggers (7) 1941 (8) Monitor (9) Africa (10) Napoleon.

Page 158, **Icy Logic**: 6-10-4-12-8-11-2-7-3-9-5-1

DECEMBER

Page 160, **Merry Christmas**: 1) YES–According to best available data, Christ was probably born between 8 B.C. and 4 B.C. The Christian Era is computed according to 6th-century reckoning to begin with the birth of Jesus A.D. 1. 2) NO–It is the Greek equivalent of CH (chi) and intends to represent Christ. 3) YES–Though the Romans decorated plants and trees, the Germans used the fir tree first and centered their celebrations around it. When Queen Victoria married Prince Albert he introduced the Christmas tree custom in England. 4) NO–It was for centuries celebrated on January 6. 5) NO–In Massachusetts in 1659 a law was passed which read: "Whosoever shall be found observing any such day as Christmas or the like, either by forebearing of labor, feasting in any other way, shall be fined 5 shillings." This law

was enforced for 22 years. Christmas did not become a legal holiday until the first half of the 19th century. 6) YES–There is also a North Pole, Alaska, and the citizens of that community have a fund set aside to answer children's requests to Santa. 7) YES–It's a giant redwood tree in California's King Canyon National Park, so designated in 1925. 8) NO–He came from Myra, Asia Minor; but his relics were stolen and brought to Bari, Italy. 9) NO–A man named B. Einar Holbell, a Danish postal clerk, thought of the plan to raise money for the needy and sick while sorting holiday mail in 1903. 10) YES–Due to the lack of books and the people's inability to read, priests and other religious leaders used to interpret the Bible through literal representation. In 1223, St. Francis in an effort to instil greater religious fervor in people set up a *praesepe* (Italian for crib) in the little village of Greccio near Assisi. 11) NO–Instead of writing a Christmas greeting to a friend, W. C. Dobson drew a group of pictures and so made the first Christmas card in 1845. 12) NO–Cows and horses. 13) YES–Because of its "heathen" origin. Frigga gave her son Balder a charm that would protect him from any injury. But Loki, an evil spirit, formed an arrow of the mistletoe, which did not grow from the elements fire, water, air, and earth from which he was supposed to be protected, and struck Balder. He was, however, saved through the intervention of several gods, and Frigga is said to bestow a kiss upon anyone standing under the mistletoe, and anyone standing under it shall be kissed. 14) YES 15) NO–It is fox hunting, but the day after Christmas is called Boxing Day. 16) NO–They are Christmas carolers in England trouping through the streets singing. 17) NO–They were wise men, not kings but magi bringing gifts of gold, myrrh, frankincense. 18) NO–Holly was used by the Roman celebrating the Saturnalia late in December, but the custom spread over Europe and then came to America. 19) NO–He is the main character in Dickens' story *A Christmas Carol*.

Page 161, **Competitive Word Games for All**: The Short Word Wins: 1) iCEd 2) astHMa 3) tRIp 4) bITe 5) aSSet 6) sTAb 7) coMMa 8) lATe 9) poSSe 10) sTIr 11) fIRe 12) druMHead 13) dECk. The Long Word Wins: 1) oracle 2) choir 3) cinders 4) eluding 5) parcels 6) cranny 7) monotones 8) barques 9) paragons 10) nectarines 11) striating 12) maligners 13) impaction

Page 162, **What Do You Really Know**

About People: THIS TEST HAS BEEN A TRAP–a trap for those who, all too rashly, think of themselves as good psychologists but fall prey to many prejudices. Scientific research has established beyond doubt that the statements lack any basis in fact. Only those persons who have answered most of the questions (if not all) with NO can say of themselves that they have preserved a sense of responsibility and thus, in truth, are the better psychologists by simply being open to other people and not judging them on the basis of one or more accidental characteristics.

Pages 162–163, **Screen Test**: Score five points for every A answer checked, 3 points for B answer, and 1 point for C. Omit ratings for items 3, 6, 9, 12, 15 because they are blanks put in for further concealment. And now for the unveiling of the test's objective: With a score of 36 to 50 you are a pessimist, one inclined to emphasize adverse aspects. A score of 20 or less would indicate that you are an optimist, one inclined to interpret events in a favorable way. The middle of the road is here indicated by a score between 21 and 35. REMEMBER: this is armchair psychology only. A bit of fun with your id.

Pages 164–165, **No answers needed**.

Pages 166–167, **How Style-Conscious Are You**: 1) a–k. 2) g–h, 3) c–r, 4) e–q, 5) d–o, 6) f–s, 7) n–p, 8) m–b, 9) i–l, 10) j–t.

Page 167, **Are You Letter Perfect**: 1) C 2) Post Office 3) Write him a letter and then another one and tell him in each! 4) FOE 5) It's safe enough but paper would be better. 6) All, of course 7) Make a large O and write name in it. 8) Mailman 9) Shorthand 10) Queue 11) Deny 12) a) CONTEMPLA-TIONS b) RESIGNATION c) CONTRA-DICTORY d) INDETERMINATE.

Page 168, **How Is Your Eye for a Mess**: Tube of paint behind stool on the right.

Page 169, **What Goes On in the Letter Circle**: For Youngsters: A) LOAF B) FIRE-STONE C) LAID D) AVER E) NOBEL F) PEAR G) TONE H) TY I) PEARL J) REST K) TYPE L) LO M) GIN N) AID O) DUN P) PEA Q) STONE R) AVE S) EARL T) FIR U) ONE V) ART W) IRE X) EAR Y) AFIRE Z) TON. For Parents: A) ARTY B) NOBEL C) IRE D) BEL E) VERDUN F) FIRE G) AIDA H) LOA I) TYPE J) STUART K) AVER L) REST M) FIRE-STONE N) PEARL O) TY P) ONEGIN Q) GIN R) NOB S) LAID T) EARL U) DUN V) STONE W) BELA X) IDA Y) AFIRE Z) LOAF.

Pages 170–171, **Family Quiz Game**. QUO-TATIONS: (1) in the XXXIII psalm (2) true; it was designed by Benjamin Franklin and minted in 1776 (3) Shakespeare (4) Thomas Paine (5) John F. Kennedy (6) Caesar (7) Nathan Hale (8) Emily Dickinson (9) Robert Frost (10) Lexington, Mass. WORDS & PHRASES: (1) the press (2) supine (3) tight-rope walker (4) I forbid (5) by the very fact (6) for the time being (7) lawyer (8) fostering mother (9) circa (about) (10) the mind is initially a clean slate. TRANSPORTATION: (1) saddle (2) the wind (3) engineer (4) run-ners (5) conductor (6) five (7) aviator (8) eight (9) slow or caution (10) caboose. PLANTS: (1) grapes (2) eucalyptus (3) palms (4) oaks (5) true (6) b (7) evergreens (8) weeds (9) the root (10) pomegranate. UNITED STATES: (1) true (2) New York City, Chicago (3) false (4) false (it was written during the War of 1812 (5) true (6) Federal Bureau of Investigation (FBI) (7) Bill of Rights (8) the Emancipation Proclamation (9) Alabama, Alaska, Arizona, Arkansas (10) true. COMPOSERS: (1) Edvard Grieg (2) Rossini (3) Franz Schubert (4) Gilbert and Sullivan (5) Tchaikovsky (6) four (7) W. C. Handy (8) Stephen Foster (9) true (10) Bob Dylan.

Page 172, **A Little Logic Among Friends**: I. Fred: 1, Alf: 6, Dave: 2, Carl: 5, Eric: 3, Gus: 4. II. Martin: 1, Lou: 2, Chas: 3, Artur: 4, Bert: 5, Dan: 6.